D1598238

Havasupai
Habitat

Havasupai Habitat

A. F. Whiting's Ethnography of a Traditional Indian Culture

Steven A. Weber & P. David Seaman
Editors

The University of Arizona Press
Tucson, Arizona

About the Editors

STEVEN A. WEBER became director of the Center for Western Studies in Flagstaff, Arizona, in 1980. He studied anthropology and biology at Northern Arizona University and combined these fields in his Ph.D. studies in anthropology at the University of Pennsylvania. He has been extensively involved in archaeological and ethnobiological research with the Hopi and the Navajo, as well as with other historic and prehistoric cultures. He has served as the president of the Society of Ethnobiology and was a co-founder and editor of the *Journal of Ethnobiology*.

P. DAVID SEAMAN, an anthropological linguist, has long been interested in American Indian studies. He was collaborating on the revision of A. F. Whiting's *Ethnobotany of the Hopi* at the time of Whiting's death in 1978. Since then he has worked on sorting and collating Whiting's extensive notes on American Indian cultures, and he has prepared a computer draft for a dictionary of the Hopi language. He earned his Ph.D. at Indiana University and joined the Department of Anthropology at Northern Arizona University in 1967.

Title-page photograph by Robert C. Euler

THE UNIVERSITY OF ARIZONA PRESS

Copyright © 1985
The Arizona Board of Regents
All Rights Reserved

This book was set in 11/13 Compugraphic 8400 Palatino.
Manufactured in the U.S.A.

Library of Congress Cataloging in Publication Data

Whiting, Alfred F.

Havasupai habitat.

Bibliography: p.
Includes index.
1. Havasupai Indians.   I. Weber, Steven A.   II. Seaman,
P. David.   III. Title.
E99.H3W47   1985   306'.08997   84-24489

ISBN 0-8165-0866-6

This is the story of the Havasupai, a group of Indians who lived on the edge of a hole as big as a mountain range. It tells how they lived off the land, finding plenty and security in a land of nothing, how they lost most of their land and their security, and how they are finding a new future in a different way of life.

A. F. WHITING

Contents

Part I

Culture and Environment

Part II

Havasupai Knowledge of the Natural World

ILLUSTRATIONS AND MAPS

TABLES

Foreword

I first met Al Whiting in the early 1950s. I was just beginning
to do anthropological research with the Walapai and the
Havasupai, and Whiting referred me to his "Havasupai Habitat" manuscript, then languishing in the vault at the Museum
of Northern Arizona. The field work had been conducted in
1941, and I was able to profit greatly from reading the report.
The data it contained helped me to prepare testimony in behalf
of the tribe's claim to their aboriginal territory. Al Whiting also
made an appearance before the U.S. Indian Claims Commission, which was hearing the case, and the tribe stands in his
debt for these contributions, as well as for his genuine friend-
ship for his Havasupai respondents.

Later, when the National Park Service was attempting to
determine the nature of Havasupai traditional use in the
Esplanade area of Grand Canyon National Park, I was able
to refer to Whiting's detailed description of the function of
that magnificent and isolated section of Grand Canyon in
Havasupai economy. His carefully recorded pages of ethnographic details provided supporting information for archaeological surveys and corroborative data for statements by
elderly Havasupai almost forty years after his initial perceptive
field work.

Although Whiting and I didn't always agree on reconstructions of Havasupai prehistory, we maintained a close contact that added to my understanding of the Havasupai. Scholars of traditional Indian cultures can profit from the work of Al Whiting, an indefatigable and exciting anthropologist until his untimely death in 1978. Thus, I was most pleased to learn that Steve Weber and Dave Seaman had resurrected "Havasupai Habitat" and had edited it for publication by the University of Arizona Press. It is most gratifying to see that these two fine scholars have been faithful to the original data and to the flavor of Whiting's pen.

Many changes have taken place in Havasupai culture and society since the time of Whiting's field work. In the 1970s they won their suit against the federal government for lands wrongfully taken from them in the past. This judgment brought more than a million dollars to the tribal treasury. Also in the 1970s, after another long battle, their pitifully small 518-acre reservation—to which they had been restricted for almost a century—was enlarged by 185,000 acres. The new boundaries returned to them a land base on the plateau above their canyon home and increased their economic potential, especially from cattle raising.

Whiting might not recognize the canyon community of Supai in the mid-1980s. Fifteen thousand tourist-hikers pass through the village each year and sightseeing planes seem almost constantly overhead. There is a new school, tourist lodge, cafe, grocery store, post office, and tribal headquarters building. Television satellite dishes in backyards bring dozens of channels into Havasupai living rooms. A private postal service delivers packages by helicopter.

On the other hand, there are many difficulties to overcome. Many modern Havasupai suffer from diabetes, alcohol abuse, and other health and psychological ills. Different factions within the tribal government cannot agree on what they want to accept from the mainstream of American society while they retain important values from their own way of life.

Whiting's early study of the Havasupai is an important ethnographic document and a valuable contribution to the anthropology of the Southwest. It is also one in which the Havasupai themselves may take pride, as tribal leaders continue their efforts to teach the younger generations about the old ways so they may take rightful pride in their culture.

ROBERT C. EULER

Acknowledgments

Many individuals and institutions have aided in the preparation of this book. The editors are grateful to D. K. Elliott and Paul M. Weber, who provided us with invaluable aid in editing the text. We are especially grateful to Mary M. Seaman, who helped with the editing, proofing, and preparation of the bibliography. We thank Dorothy House, head librarian at the Museum of Northern Arizona research center, who assisted us in our exhaustive search for all of Whiting's Havasupai writings. Tomas A. Stierhoff helped update the bird section, Steven D. Emslie and Terry A. Vaughan gave assistance in updating the terms used in the chapter on animals, and Richard H. Hevly helped to bring the scientific plant terminology up to date. The editors are especially grateful to Gary Nabhan and Robert C. Euler, both of whom read the manuscript and offered helpful suggestions and support. Dr. Euler also generously gave the editors permission to use appropriate photographs from his collections. And finally, the editors appreciate the positive and helpful professional input received from the staff at the University of Arizona Press.

Over the years many people helped Alfred F. Whiting in his work with the Havasupai. It was under the guidance of Dr. and Mrs. Harold S. Colton that Whiting first became acquainted with the Southwest. Under the direction of Dr. Colton, the Museum of Northern Arizona helped finance much of Whiting's field work and provided him with office space. Edwin McKee, head naturalist at Grand Canyon National Park, first introduced Whiting to the Havasupai and also offered many helpful suggestions on Havasupai basketry.

A. F. Whiting's research was aided by Mr. and Mrs. C. F. Schaffer, a Mr. Heacock of the statistical division at the office of Indian Affairs, a Miss VerNooy of the University of Chicago Library, and by the librarians at the University of Arizona Library, the Arizona Pioneers Historical Society, and the Library of the State of Arizona.

Whiting was assisted throughout his Havasupai field work by his wife, Dorothy West Whiting, who compiled the data on food preparation and the manufacture of Havasupai basketry. Through the faculty of the Department of Anthropology at the University of Chicago, he received stimulus, direction, and financial aid.

Sarah J. Tucker assisted Whiting in the use of the Walapai manuscript material. James H. Hall, Jr., helped on the Havasupai linguistic section and aided in some of the field work. Edward H. and Rosamond Spicer gave helpful criticism and suggestions during all stages of Whiting's work.

Finally, R. H. Peebles, Earl Jackson, Allan Phillips, C. O. Lampland, and John C. McGregor all contributed their aid and assistance within their specialties. Their help is specifically documented in the portions of the text with which they were concerned.

To all these people, their institutions, and the numerous Havasupai, Walapai, and Hopi who made his Havasupai research possible, Whiting often acknowledged his deep indebtedness.

Alfred F. Whiting and the Havasupai Indians

In the early 1920s Alfred F. Whiting became interested in ethnobotany while studying with a University of Michigan expedition to Mexico. This interest was reinforced through his work as Curator of Botany at the Museum of Northern Arizona in the late 1930s, during which period he completed his *Ethnobotany of the Hopi*.

From 1938 to 1940 Whiting pursued studies toward a Ph.D. at the University of Chicago, and his work among the Havasupai was to have been the basis for his dissertation in ethnobiology. It was around this time, however, that a pattern was established which was to prevail throughout his life. He would enthusiastically enter a project, do extremely careful and competent work resulting in massive and valuable accumulations of original information, and then drop that project in favor of some other equally attractive academic adventure. He did not ever willingly sit down and finish up his notes into a publishable report or book, and he never did complete his formal degree. On the other hand, he accumulated for posterity a vast wealth of field work (reaching nearly seventy-five linear feet of shelf space), far more than would ordinarily be expected from any one individual researcher. *

---

* Further information about the nature and extent of information in the A. F. Whiting Indian Archives may be obtained by contacting Dr. P. David Seaman, Northern Arizona University, Flagstaff, Arizona 86011.

Whiting always checked and rechecked his data both in the field and with as many specialists as he could find on the particular topic under consideration. His impressive professional correspondence is indicative of his attention to detail and of his generosity in sharing any information he had with other students and professionals who asked him about any topic in the areas of his expertise. Most of the specialists with whom he shared his knowledge gave credit to Whiting in their own subsequent publications, but his letters reveal that some did not.

Whiting was a successful Curator of Anthropology at Dartmouth Museum, one of the oldest museums in the United States. He did much to update and improve the collections there, and he convinced the Dartmouth constituency of the relevance of such a museum in an academic setting. His greatest pleasure was in challenging students, and he was acknowledged as an effective and innovative teacher who gave of himself unstintingly in personal and professional advice and encouragement.

Whiting's wry humor stood him in good stead throughout his life and was appreciated by all who knew him. At Dartmouth, for example, he taught field work techniques by encouraging his students to question a fictitious "Mr. Ka-Hopi," who visited the classroom and served Hopi mutton stew to his inquisitive "guests." His last report to the Dartmouth Anthropology Department, which he dictated from a Flagstaff hospital bed three days before his death, was entitled "Final Report of an Add-Junk Professor."

∽

Whiting's initial field work for this book was designed to be a rather brief ethnobotanical supplement to Leslie Spier's (1928) classic study of the Havasupai. His objective was to supplement Spier's work in the area where he felt it appeared weakest: the identification of plants used by the Havasupai when they lived on the Coconino Plateau.* Whiting's planned two-month field season, in 1941, eventually expanded into a nine-month season covering such research areas as ethnozoology, rocks and minerals, weather and astronomy, and observations about culture and culture change. By 1950 Whiting had completed a number of preliminary revisions of a manuscript entitled "Havasupai Habitat," which described his observations and which covered such a variety of subjects that it was actually a fairly complete ethnography of these Indians.

Whiting died in 1978 without having published his "Havasupai Habitat" manuscript. At the time of his death, the manuscript was still in rough form. As Whiting realized, extensive editing was needed before the manuscript could be published in book form. In accomplishing the editing task, we found that changes and updating were necessary in all sections of the manuscript, on practically every page, so it was not feasible to separate the editors' work from Whiting's. The basic information and general format are his, while later errors that may have crept in during editing are ours.

There are two parts to this book. The first is a thematic, ethnographic description of the Havasupai. It includes information necessary to familiarize the reader with how the Havasupai lived as they did at the time of Whiting's visit. Although many of the descriptions of Havasupai culture have been published previously by others, we thought it was important to repeat some of these descriptions so that the reader would have a clear and complete picture. On the other hand, it was our intent that his book describe as many of Whiting's original observations as possible, while not excessively repeating information that can be obtained in other published works. Therefore, repetitious information has been kept to a minimum and some chapters, such as "The People," which describes

---

* The Coconino Plateau refers to the "up-top" plateau along the south rim of the Grand Canyon, and not to the Tonto Plateau within the Canyon itself.

Havasupai history and territory, have been kept intentionally brief. In the decades that have passed since Whiting's study, a number of the observations he described may differ somewhat from what exists in Havasupai society in the mid-1980s. For this reason we have, whenever possible, referred the reader to more recent works or other possible interpretations of Havasupai culture.

Part II of the book is made up of lists of terms broken down into four subject areas. Each term is defined, written phonetically, and its usage or Havasupai knowledge of it described. The lists on weather and astronomy (Chapter 11) and minerals, metals, and rocks (Chapter 12) are presented alphabetically by the English or scientific name (except for the section on fixed stars, which is arranged in calendar order). The lists of animals (Chapter 13) and plants (Chapter 14) are grouped into their respective taxonomic sequences and arranged alphabetically by scientific name within each category. Some identifications are at the class or order level while others are at the family, genus, or species levels. The taxonomic category of the identified plant or animal was dependent upon Havasupai usage. At times the Havasupai distinguished the species of some plants and animals, while at other times they grouped everything into one general category with one term. An asterisk preceding the scientific name has been used in tables and lists throughout the book to indicate an introduced or domesticated species.

The orthographic system used for Havasupai words throughout the book is based upon the International Phonetic Alphabet, which is widely used in anthropological field work. A pronunciation key for Havasupai language sounds is given in Chapter 2. An asterisk in front of a Havasupai term indicates that it is either a reconstructed form or part of a longer form.

∽

Although Whiting's personal life was burdened by family tragedies, his professional life was a celebration, through careful observation, of the life and survival techniques of little-known peoples in the western United States and elsewhere. The manuscript on which this book is based is a good example of the enduring legacy Al Whiting left in the field of ethnography. It is a detailed documentation of the Havasupai Indian environment and how these people survived within it.

STEVEN A. WEBER
P. DAVID SEAMAN

PART I

Culture and Environment

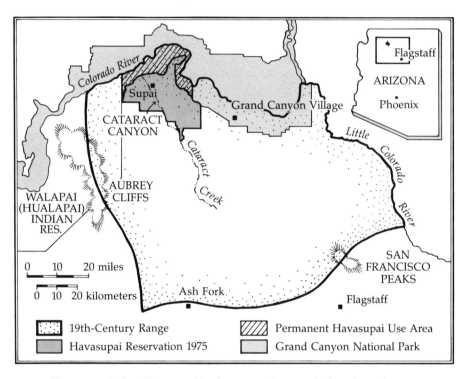

Havasuapi Indian Territory, Northwestern Arizona. Before the mid-nineteenth century the Havasupai hunted and gathered over an area twice the size of Rhode Island. During the next few decades their old range was drastically reduced by the growth of national park and forest lands, and by 1882 they were legally restricted to a 518-acre reservation around the village of Supai. In 1975 after lengthy court battles, the reservation was expanded by 185,000 acres and the law allocated another 95,300 acres of the Grand Canyon National Park for permanent use by the Havasupai.

1. The People and Their Land

The Havasupai are a small band of Yuman-speaking Indians who live in a deep canyon that forms a branch of the Grand Canyon in north central Arizona. The word *Havasupai* means "the people who live at the place which is green." It is often translated as "the people of the blue-green waters," in direct and conscious parallel to Charles Cadman's "Land of the Sky-blue Water," a reference which is as euphonic and romantic as it is incorrect and unjustified.* Those who, after a long drive, have ridden or tramped the dry, weary trail down to the small village know that the name "people of the place which is green" signifies far more of romance and beauty than "blue-water people." This place which is green is hidden amid a wilderness of rock three thousand feet below the rim of that canyon, which, with all true meaning of the word, is justly called "Grand." It is a tiny patch of green land, a thin strip of fertility tortured into a shape such as Dali might use to paint an emerald.

---

* Whiting based this conclusion on information in a letter from Charles Cadman to Edwin D. McKee. The letter was in the files of the Grand Canyon Natural History Association (by 1984 it had been transferred to the files of the Grand Canyon National Park Study Collection). *Havasu* means "blue" or "green," not "blue-green." The initial *ha* does not mean water, but is part of the color term.

Flanked at its lower edge with waterfalls instead of diamond chips, this emerald area is inlaid among the raw reds, purples, and yellows of one of the most rugged portions of the world's surface. Less than a quarter of a mile wide at any point, the "place which is green" begins with the sudden appearance of a river which rises as if by magic out of dry gravel. For less than three miles it burbles, ripples, and purrs, letting a minute portion of its body be deflected into garden plots and pastures. After a series of waterfalls, each more beautiful than the last, it flings itself into space, and, with a mighty roar, disappears into the depths of a dark, narrow, and virtually impassable gorge.

Over the years since white men first came to Arizona, the people of the canyon have left their own ways, and now are mingling with the greater stream of Euro-American ways of life. And yet, for a time, they have tended to retain, even in this new channel, much of their old ways of life and thought. If we could but know how it is that different types of water—or men—can occupy the same channel and then blend into one, how much better could we plan our river developments and our handling of strangers within our midst.

THE POPULATION

Intermarriage of the Havasupai with their western neighbors, the Walapai (Hualapai) was frequent, and they often spoke of themselves as if they were only a band of that larger tribe. The Havasupai may have included two incipient bands; see Dobyns and Euler (1970, p. 18). It was probably only an accident of administrative history that the government in 1882 designated them as an independent group. In 1941 the Havasupai numbered about fifty households, totaling between 150 to 175 individuals. At that time a few families lived outside Cataract Canyon,* near the settlement at Grand Canyon Village, where they

---

* By the 1980s Cataract Canyon was usually referred to as Havasu Canyon. However, in this book, Whiting's frequent references to Cataract Canyon have been left intact. The official name of the settlement is "Grand Canyon"; however, to avoid ambiguity Whiting decided to refer to the community—which consists of several hotels, tourist camps, and Park Service offices, living quarters, museums, etc.—as "Grand Canyon Village."

Havasu Falls, the third in a series of five waterfalls in Cataract Canyon, is located about two miles northwest of the village of Supai. Photo by Carma Lee Smithson, 1962; courtesy of Robert C. Euler.

worked for the railroad, the National Park Service, or found other employment within the community.

In former times the ancestors of the group which we know as the Havasupai were more numerous and had a much larger territory at their disposal. Early estimates indicate that during the first half of the nineteenth century the population of the Havasupai may have been as high as 300 or perhaps even slightly higher.* Irregular counts between 1870 and 1895 indicate that the population decreased from a possible maximum of 275 to probably not less than 225. Between 1898 and 1906 there was a sharp drop in the population from 261 to 166 resulting from a series of epidemics and unhealthful conditions caused by the sudden influx of miners, overcrowding in the school, and temporary poor housing conditions caused by a disastrous flood.

Following these discouraging events the population gradually recovered so that by 1941, in spite of occasional epidemics, it was approaching its former levels. Intermarriage and migration to other tribes masked this population gain. The actual 1941 population within the village at Cataract Canyon was only slightly above that reported for the group twenty years before (Whiting 1943).

HAVASUPAI TERRITORY

The Havasupai claim that prior to 1850 they occupied, virtually without competition, an area equal in size to the state of Delaware. They ranged from what is now the eastern portion of the Walapai Reservation east to the Little Colorado River. In 1776 they had settlements farther east in what is now Hopi

---

* Havasupai population figures are controversial. Whiting's research papers contain over 400 pages of notes related to this topic. Whiting arrived at the figures given here after painstaking analysis of U.S. Commissioner of Indian Affairs Annual Reports for 1849 through 1943, and of numerous other documents cited in the bibliography of this book.

territory near Moenkopi (Coues 1900) although these may have been only occasional camps. They easily ranged as far south as Flagstaff and possibly as far as the area of the Tonto Apache in central Arizona. They camped along the northern range of the Yavapai as far west as Ashfork. The concentration of population throughout most of this area probably was not sufficiently high to constitute occupancy in any real sense. Rather, this was an area over which occasional family groups wandered on hunting expeditions. They almost certainly did not attempt to defend this area against intruders, and there is no indication that they ever felt that other hunting parties, which they met in these areas, were trespassing.

For the most part the Havasupai lived just south of the Colorado River. Within this territory they utilized three different kinds of land: the agricultural plots deep in Cataract Canyon, an intermediate shelf (or "Esplanade"), and an area of winter camps near the Grand Canyon rim of the Coconino Plateau. There were few agricultural areas, all of them small and in incredibly difficult terrain. The most important location was the area of the village in Cataract Canyon, which is isolated from the surrounding territory by a double row of cliffs several hundred feet high. In 1941 there were two trails commonly used to enter this canyon. These were improved trails which had been worked on with dynamite and pickaxe. In aboriginal times narrow foot trails, part of which were literally ladders, were quite sufficient. Some of these offered much more direct access to the village area than do the modern horse trails. E. U. spoke casually of driving a car to the head of such a trail, climbing down the trail to the village, and returning within a twenty-four-hour period. This activity was performed repeatedly by the Havasupai as a matter of course.

Below the village the canyon becomes too narrow for any agricultural use, and the roughness of the terrain, combined with virulent tradition, bars the Indians from penetrating farther. To the west of Cataract Canyon the Plateau is high, dry, and barren for many miles until one comes to Mono Canyon,* a small tributary of the Grand Canyon. Here the Havasupai said that they once had some fields, but that they were gradually forced out of the area by eastward pressure of the Walapai. This is a controversial matter, not supported by available evidence.

In addition to these areas within Cataract Canyon, there were a few other small areas where some crops were raised. The Bright Angel Trail leads from the South Rim of the Grand Canyon, near the hotels and post office, to the North Rim. This duplicates, in part, an old Havasupai Indian trail. At the base of the first descent is a small garden plot, known today as Indian Gardens, which was formerly cultivated by some of the Havasupai. Below this area is a passage which leads down through the inner gorge to the Colorado River itself. Once the Colorado is crossed, the trail leads to the North Rim and the ancient territory of the Southern Paiute. Historically, this passage route was used not only by the Havasupai, but by their enemies, the Yavapai and the Southern Paiute, as well.† There were other places at which the Grand Canyon could be crossed, but this was the main trail and the one most often used. The trail made Indian Gardens a dangerous area in which to farm and reduced the Havasupai's chances of being able to collect the harvest for their own use. In addition to these isolated farm lands, the Havasupai have spoken of several places on the Plateau where farming was tried, but none of these was very successful.

Between the level of the village in the bottom of Cataract Canyon and the Plateau is the Esplanade. This shelf or platform extends from the top edge of the inner gorge to the base of the cliffs that form the south edge of the main canyon and its tributaries. The Esplanade is similar to the lower shelf farther

---

* In the 1980s Mono Canyon was also called Moho Canyon or Mohawk Canyon.

† As of 1985 anthropologists had found no conclusive evidence that the Yavapai used the Bright Angel Trail or that the Southern Paiute were continual enemies of the Havasupai.

east in the Grand Canyon known as the Tonto Platform. At the base of the cliffs along the southern edge of this platform are several springs. These springs, as well as a number of water holes, were more reliable than those on the Plateau. Because some of the springs could be used throughout the year, the Havasupai were able to keep their horses in small, isolated pasture areas on the Esplanade, where they would not wander into other areas. Though it is often difficult to descend from the Plateau to these platforms, once they are reached travel is a simple matter. Many well-marked trails lead from one part of the Esplanade to another.

The Plateau, especially the area along the South Rim of the Grand Canyon, was the real homeland of the Havasupai. The Esplanade was a fine place to collect mescal and a good place for temporary camps in dry weather, and the garden areas in the canyon were centers of activity, but these were not living areas. The Havasupai said, "We used to live on top all the time. We just had gardens in the canyon." Here on the high Plateau, with its dense covering of pinyon and juniper and pine, where the antelope were abundant, the Havasupai really felt at home.

THE ANNUAL CYCLE OF ACTIVITIES

During the years before the Havasupai were restricted to their present reservation at the bottom of Cataract Canyon, their annual round of activities brought them into various parts of their extensive range. As spring approached, the scattered family groups made their way to their garden plots. Here they cleared the ground of last year's debris, repaired the ditches, and with their neighbors' help, built low earth and brush dams to deflect the water from the river. After the fields had been planted and irrigated once or twice, family groups would wander back onto the Plateau to hunt game, collect fresh greens, and visit with other families whom they might meet. Occasional trips would be made back to the fields to irrigate, weed, and inspect the growing crop. As green corn became available and the springs and water holes on the Plateau began to dry out, more and more families began to camp near their fields, either in dome-shaped brush shelters or in the caves which overlooked the valley. At this time it was necessary to guard the crops, not only from marauding bands of Yavapai, but from rodents and other pests native to the area. This did not prevent occasional hunting or mining expeditions or, if life got really boring, a raid on the Paiute* north of Grand Canyon.

As the crops ripened everyone gathered around the fields. Invitations were sent to the Hopi and the Walapai for a harvest festival, usually held in late August. After this period of festivity came the main harvest of the crops. Each family collected corn, beans, and dried squash and carefully selected seeds for the following season. The food was stored in small walled granaries in the rock cliffs high above any possible flood waters. As the chilling winds of autumn began to whine down the now-dusky canyon, group after group returned to the Plateau. In seasons when the pinyon crop was good, a considerable portion of the tribe might still be found together on the Plateau late in the fall.

As winter approached, they broke up into small family bands and wandered off by themselves to establish winter camps. Often several families settled within a short distance of each other. Here they built conical huts covered with brush and earth. One such cluster still existed in 1941. From these semi-permanent camps individuals or groups of men from several households would go off on hunting expeditions. There was little wild plant food to be gathered during this season. Therefore, the women spent their time with wood gathering, caring for the children, and other household duties. As food ran low, occasional trips would be made back to the vicinity of the fields and storehouses.

While there seems to have been considerable variation in the habits of individual family groups, each family had a more or less characteristic route which it followed season after season.

---

* As of 1985 there was no conclusive archaeological evidence that the Havasupai ever crossed the Grand Canyon to raid the Paiute.

These were generally known to other members of the group, and they could, thus, locate other families when necessary. Although the band had no fixed or clearly defined winter social activities, there was probably a great deal of inter-family contact.

The Havasupai were not as remote and isolated a people as popular writers seem to think. During the fall and winter periods certain families drifted east and spent a month or more in the Hopi towns, helping with the harvest, observing dances, and talking with visitors from other pueblos. Intermarriage with the Hopi rarely took place. Nevertheless, close relationships between specific Hopi and Havasupai families were maintained year after year. The Hopi towns were strictly neutral territory, so that trade and peace talks between the Havasupai and their enemies were sometimes conducted under the surveillance of a Hopi chief. Havasupai contacts were primarily with the people of Oraibi, the westernmost of the Hopi towns, but some contact with the eastern Hopi villages was undoubtedly established.

Some families wandered west from Cataract Canyon to spend the winter with the Walapai. Here again, they met members of other tribes such as the Paiute from the north and the Mohave from the Lower Colorado. Havasupai relationships with the Paiute and Mohave were often hostile, except under Walapai sponsorship.

CONTACT WITH OUTSIDERS

Spanish influences, which reached the Hopi in strength after 1600, were passed on to the Havasupai through trade and, occasionally, through direct contact with Spaniards in the Hopi towns. By 1776, when Father Francisco Garcés visited their village in Cataract Canyon, the Havasupai were already acquainted with many aspects of Spanish-American culture (Coues 1900). The trade routes that had existed in prehistoric times continued to function, and Spanish influences passed westward along these trails.

After 1820 Spanish contacts with the Hopi virtually ceased. By 1833 American trappers had begun to explore the area, but they had little effect on the culture of the Hopi or their western neighbors. The most important effect on the Havasupai at this time was the gradual but persistent curtailment of their range. On the west the Walapai, who were being forced east by other groups, began to replace the Havasupai, especially in Mono Canyon. Varying historical interpretations exist on whether such displacement of the Havasupai occurred; see, for example, Euler (1974a). On the east, the Navajo were beginning to occupy the territory between the Hopi towns and the easternmost semi-permanent camps of the Havasupai. It was not until after the U.S. Civil War that direct contact between the Euro-Americans and Havasupai became significant.

With the discovery of gold in the Prescott area in 1863 (Farish 1916), a flood of miners and prospectors poured into northern Arizona. Some found their way down into the branches of the Grand Canyon. A deposit of lead was discovered in Cataract Canyon (*The Miner*, 1880) below the farm lands of the Havasupai. Because of the decrease in former Havasupai territory and resources, these farm lands had become the main focus of the Indians' activities and the backbone of their economy. The development of mines directly below the village, with the subsequent need for living quarters, mills, and shops, was a direct threat to the Havasupai. The situation came to the attention of the military authorities, by whose quick action the farm-village area was made a reservation by presidential proclamation. No one, the Indians included, ever suspected that any further area need be reserved for their special use.

As tourist interest in the Grand Canyon continued to grow, and as cattlemen occupied more of the old Havasupai range, the Indians were forced back onto their little, irrigated farm plots in Cataract Canyon. By 1895 the U.S. Government had reluctantly established a school and an agency within the Canyon. By the early 1900s, the Havasupai found themselves shut off from their old range by the expansion of National Park and National Forest lands. The limited area within Cataract Canyon had never been an adequate area to sustain all the Havasupai throughout the year, and their economic situation became and remained acute. Many Indians were forced to seek outside employment, of which little existed in the area.

By the 1940s the number of winter residents on the Plateau had declined. A family with school-age children tended to reside in the canyon during the winter months. Thus, the houses on the Plateau were only temporarily occupied during certain seasons, such as the pinyon harvest or the hunting season.

THE HAVASUPAI IN 1941

The vast horde of tourists who visit the Grand Canyon each year take very little notice of the Havasupai, and, apart from the work of the Indian Service and Park Service, there has been little organized interest in the Havasupai. By 1941 there were some casual activities organized by the Indian Service teachers, but there was relatively little missionary work. After 1941 the Episcopal Church took a direct interest in the Havasupai and by 1950 actively maintained a resident missionary and a church in the village in Cataract Canyon. The church,* an adapted quonset hut, had been flown in by helicopter.

In 1940–1941 there were about fifty families living in Supai, the Havasupai village in Cataract Canyon. Three or four families lived at Grand Canyon Village and several others were scattered on the Plateau or among the Walapai. There were two trails by which the village in Cataract Canyon could be reached. A nine-mile trail led from the rim to the west side of Cataract Canyon. This trail, however, was over sixty miles north of the main highway and the nearest settlement. The other trail, thirty-five miles west of Grand Canyon Village, was

---

* By 1985 the Episcopal Church was no longer active in Supai, and the church building there had been taken over by a fundamentalist group.

Aerial view of Supai, Arizona, in 1977. Photo by Robert C. Euler.

about thirteen miles long and was the more usual route for tourist and Indian travel. Over this trail the semi-weekly mail was packed into the village on government mules. An unreliable telephone line connected the agency with Grand Canyon Village and the agency was also in communication with Grand Canyon Park Service Headquarters by shortwave radio.

Havasupai contact with the world outside their canyon home was increasing in 1941. Contact with Indians of other tribes continued when visitors came to Cataract Canyon for the fall harvest festival. In addition, most of them left at frequent intervals for shopping, visiting, or for work. The annual fourth of July Indian Powwow at Flagstaff was particularly popular. Here the Havasupai came in contact with large numbers of Hopi, Navajo, Walapai, and members of many other tribes. A rodeo at Grand Canyon likewise attracted many Havasupai, both as visitors and participants.

The only non-indigenous people living in Cataract Canyon in 1941 were a resident nurse; members of the agency staff; the sub-agent in charge, who was also the resident farmer; and his wife, who taught school. (The school was divided into two groups, and in the absence of a second teacher a local Havasupai girl with a high-school education would substitute.) It was through this group that the Havasupai maintained their contact with the outside world. Like the agent's wife, they ordered food from the store at Grand Canyon Village over the agency telephone. The nurse also served as a postmistress, and she and the school teacher spent many hours helping Havasupai fill out order forms for mail-order houses. Through these same channels, a high-school education and hospital care were made available at the main agency at Truxton Canyon.

2. The Ways of Words

The language of the Havasupai evolved from an ancestral Hokan stock. It is, with some minor exceptions, identical to the language of the Walapai and is apparently only slightly divergent from that of the Yavapai. Although in phonetic structure Havasupai also closely resembles the lowland Yuman languages (such as Mohave, for example), and the number of cognates is very high, Havasupai speakers cannot understand any of those languages. Havasupai, thus, forms—along with the dialects of the Walapai and Yavapai—a northeastern group of Yuman languages.

Whiting did not claim to be a linguist, although his field notes include thousands of pages of careful linguistic work for several American Indian languages. Before his death in 1978, Whiting had been discussing ideas for updating his linguistic work in Havasupai and Hopi with one of the editors of this book. Thus, the information on the Havasupai language presented in this chapter consists primarily of early notes which Whiting was in the process of revising. More recent information on the nature and status of the Havasupai language can be obtained from the reports of linguistic investigators such as Seiden (1963), Redden (1966a, 1966b, 1976a, 1976b, 1977), Winter (1957, 1967), Kozlowski (1972, 1976a, 1976b), Voegelin and Voegelin (1977), and others mentioned in the bibliography.

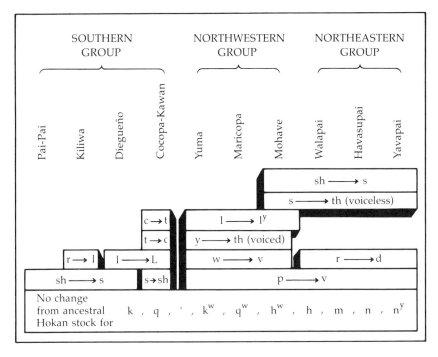

Evolution of Phonemes in Yuman Languages

YUMAN LANGUAGES

Kroeber (1943) has noted that Havasupai tends to resemble Paipai of Baja California, probably because intermediate languages tend to develop a series of phonetic shifts which make them sound different even when the basic vocabulary and grammar remain largely unchanged. Although Paipai and the northeastern Yuman languages have remained relatively undifferentiated, they are linguistically, as well as geographically, at opposite ends of the group. Paipai exhibits only one change from the ancestral Hokan stock, which it shares with Kiliwa and Dieguño. Dieguño, in turn, shares a change with the relatively specialized Cocopa-Kawan language. These southern Yuman languages (with one exception) share no changes with Yuma, Maricopa, and Mohave, which form a

closely allied (northwestern) group along the lower Colorado
and adjacent Gila river. The Walapai-Havasupai-Yavapai
(northeastern) languages do not share all of these specializa-
tions, but they have participated in some of them. There also
appears to be a case of independent development which occurs
in Cocopa-Kawan, in Mohave, and in the northeastern group.
In these languages what appears to have been an ancestral *sh*
has become *s*. Among the Mohave and the northeastern group
this change is apparently related to the change of *s* into *th*.
There is no corresponding change in Cocopa-Kawan, but there
is a parallel *sh* to *s* shift in the other southern Yuman languages.
Thus, throughout the southern group, the ancestral distinction
between *s* and *sh* has been neutralized. These shifts, considered
together with the widely separated geographic gap, would seem
to indicate independent parallel developments.

The basic resemblances between Paipai and the northeastern
group of Yuman languages can be attributed to the fact that
they are both marginal and both relatively close to the patterns
of their ancestral Hokan stock. Also for this reason, Havasupai
tends to show, as well as any of the Yuman languages, relationships with other languages of the Hokan stock. The interrelationships within this larger group have not been worked out
in detail in a satisfactory manner. This is particularly true of
the southern members of the group. The northern Hokan languages—including Karok, Shasta-Achomawi, Chimariko, Yana
and Pomo (all of California)—have been examined in some
detail, and their interrelationships are fairly clear (Sapir 1917).
The relationships between Yuman and the southern Californian
Chumash, Esselen, Salinan, and possibly Costanoan, are not as
well understood, due, in part, to the fact that they are now
largely extinct and the data are limited. Cochimi, which was
spoken in several closely allied dialects in Baja California, and
Seri (along the coast of Sonora), together with Chontal
(Tequistlatecan) of Oaxaca, are obviously allied with the
Hokan group in some way. Cochimi appears to be closer than
either of the others to unspecialized Yuman, but the data are

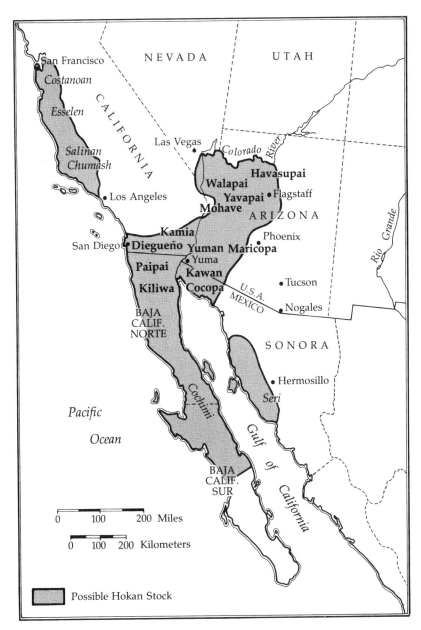

Distribution of Yuman languages from Hokan stock. Languages more closely related to Havasupai are shown in boldface type. Some other possible Hokan relatives are shown in italic type.

TABLE 2.1
Linguistic Description of Havasupai Consonants

	Labial	Apical	Velar	Glottal
Stops:	p	t d	k q	ʔ
Labialized:			k^w q^w	h^w
Fricatives:	f v	th s		h
Laterals:		l	k^l q^l	
Affricate:		c		
Nasals:	m	n n^y		
Semi-vowels:	w	y		

very weak and not well analyzed. Until a concentrated analysis is completed for this problem, the relationships between these various languages will remain in doubt. Because of its relative conservatism within the Yuman group, Havasupai is an important source of comparative data for such a study. It does, however, have certain specialized phonetic changes and its own peculiarities of vocabulary and, probably, of grammar. It cannot be taken as a pure example of the ancestral form of the various Yuman languages, though it may approximate it more than many of the others, especially the adjacent northeastern Yuman group of Mohave-Yuma-Maricopa on the lower Colorado River.

PHONETICS

Consonants

About two dozen consonant sounds might be distinguished by non-natives trying to record Havasupai speech phonetically. Table 2.1 is a linguistic description of these consonants. The raised letters of the International Phonetic Alphabet shown in Table 2.1 have been lowered to standard position in the text (Parts I and II) of this book. A few of the IPA distinctions shown in the table are finer than those recorded by some linguists. An attempt has been made to record the native terms in a way that would be understandable if the sounds were repeated to a Havasupai speaker. Table 2.2 is a pronunciation guide for Havasupai consonants showing both the orthographic symbol used in the text and the closest equivalent English sound of the symbol.

Vowels

The distinction between long and short vowels is important in Havasupai. Long vowels are stressed, more clearly enunciated, held longer, and are usually at a slightly higher pitch than short vowels. In addition, some vowels actually change sound when they are shortened. All these distinctions can only be approximated with English examples (Table 2.3).

Other Phonetic Features

The distinction between *i* and *y* is at times difficult to determine. Probably there is little, if any, phonetic difference. There are situations where Havasupai *y* is cognate with Maricopa and Yuma *th*. In such cases it is clear that the Havasupai should be read *y* and not *i*. The validity of the diphthong *ai* is in doubt. It is possible that it should always be considered as *ay* or *ayi*.

The Havasupai *a* is subject to several modifications. Initial unstressed *a* is often weakly pronounced and difficult to hear. It is dropped in long words when the stress is not near the beginning of the word, as in '*apa'a* "man." The *a* before *ny, l, y* or *i* frequently is pronounced as if it were *i* or *e*:

halo'o becomes *helo'o* "rabbit"
anya-ca becomes *inyaca* or *-enyaca* "black"
**ta–yace* becomes *ti–yace* (cf. Maricopa *ta–thic*) "corn"

The *w* is likely to absorb an adjacent *a*; thus *u* plus *va* becomes *u-wa*. The *m* tends to change an adjacent *a*, rendering

---

* A linguistic term in this chapter preceded by an asterisk is either a reconstructed form or a portion of a longer form.

TABLE 2.2
Pronunciation Guide for Havasupai Consonants

Orthographic Symbol	Approximate Equivalent Sound in English
c	As in *c*hurch; oftentimes voiced, as in *j*erk
d	As in *d*ell; sometimes with a trilled variation
f	Almost as in *f*un; a closer approximation is the Spanish bilabial *f,* as in *f*iesta; probably the same phoneme as *v*
h	As in *h*appy; somewhat stronger than in English, but apparently not as marked as in other Yuman languages
hw	As in northeastern U.S. English *wh*ich or *wh*ere (contrast *w*itch and *w*ear)
k	As in *k*ill; often pronounced *g,* as in *g*ill
kl	As in *cl*ean (*k* with an *l* release); or as in *gl*ean (*g* with an *l* release)
kw	As in *qu*een; often pronounced *gw* in Havasupai
l	As in *l*ip; rarely, voiceless *L,* as in softly spoken p*l*ay
m	As in *m*iss; the sound may be held longer in some situations
n	As in *n*o
ny	Almost as in ca*ny*on or pi*ny*on; similar to Spanish ca*ñ*on
p	As in *p*it; rarely, *b* as in *b*it
q	Almost as in *c*aught (a *k*-sound, but pronounced farther back in the mouth); sometimes this sound is of very short duration
ql	Almost as the *kl* in *cl*ean (see above), but pronounced farther back in the mouth (*q* with an *l* release)
qw	Almost as the *kw* in *qu*een (see above) but pronounced farther back in the mouth
s	As in *s*hip; rarely, if ever, *z,* as in *z*ero
t	As in *t*ell; sometimes the sound is of very short duration, and is positioned a little farther back in the mouth than a regular English *t*
th	As in *th*ere or *th*ing (the voicing varies)
v	Almost as in *v*ery; a closer approximation is the Spanish bilabial *v,* as in *v*e*n*ir
w	As in *w*in
y	As in e*y*e or *y*es; (consonantal *i*)
'	Glottal stop (contrast the sounds of "a <u>n</u>ice man" and "a<u>n ī</u>ce man")

NOTE: The raised orthography of the IPA system has been lowered to standard position in this table and throughout the text of this book.

TABLE 2.3
Havasupai Vowel Sounds

Orthographic Symbol of Long Vowel	Equivalent Sound in English	Orthographic Symbol of Short Vowel	Equivalent Sound in English
ii	As in piece	i	As in pith
ee	As in bed	e	As in bet
aa	As in father	a	As in pat
oo	As in odd	o	As in otter
uu	As in too	u	As in put

it indistinct. The *m* may also be long: *ammalaka* "woodrat," *ammha'a* "gourd," *hammanya* "child." In general, -*i*- will apparently absorb a preceding *a*; thus *ka* plus *i* gives *ki*. For example, **-ka-nya-wa-i-va* "shut up in his house" becomes -*ki-ny-we-va*.

When words are said in isolation, they naturally tend to become exaggerated. With requests for constant repeating and precision, long sounds—especially long vowels—tend to pulsate and even to break up into two seemingly distinct syllables. In Yuma the end of the sentence often has a repeated vowel; in Havasupai all words spoken in isolation—as in a list—seem to be treated in this exaggerated fashion. When a stressed vowel is final, it is followed by a glottal stop and an echo of the vowel. This may be reduced to a whisper or a mere syllabic pulsating of the vowel. Such repeated vowels are not retained when a word is compounded with a following word. An unstressed final vowel is not repeated in this manner, except in the case of a few borrowed words.

Most (but certainly not all) Havasupai words follow a consonant-vowel pattern of *CVCV, CV'V, CVCV'V,* or *CVCVCVCV.* Consonantal clusters do occur, usually with only two consonants, rarely with three. These clusters usually contain *s, n, l,* or *m.* Groups of two or more complete stops apparently do not occur, with the possible exception of a glottal stop followed by another consonant stop (such as *p, t,* or *k*).

TABLE 2.4
Modification of Linguistic Roots

Modification Technique	English Example	Havasupai Example	
Root	man	*yu'u*	"eye"
Prefix	wo-man	*'i-yu'u*	"he of the eyes," specifically "owl"
Suffix	man-ly	*yu-nym'i*	"eye-fur," specifically "eyebrow"
Root	unknown	*'akuula'*	"jackrabbit"
Infix	un-be-known[1]	*k-ah-uula*	"rabbit-skin blanket"
Root	goose	*awiiqeca*	rock
Ablaut	geese	*awiiqaca*	"a lot of rocks"

[1]The infix does not really occur in English; this example attempts to give at least the "feel" of it.

MORPHOLOGY

Through the processes of modification linguistic roots can be elaborated into forms which have a related meaning. The term "theme" has been applied to both simple and elaborated roots. Several themes can be combined into a single expression, some of which become quite long and complicated in Havasupai. In such cases there is a marked tendency to abbreviate, often by dropping an initial unstressed *a*. Compare, for example, *aqwaka* "deer" and *qwakata* "elk." In other cases, a portion of a familiar component part may be dropped: *ici-hwanyamo-valecikaava* "fern bush" is often heard as *hwanyamovalecikaava*.

In many cases meaning is restricted to a very specific type within the possible range of literal meaning. For example, compare *qwa* "to have horns" and *qwa-ka* "someone who has horns," specifically "deer." *Amu* is the name of the mountain sheep, but this term occurs in many compounds as if it originally meant "some kind of animal." For example *amu-qwatha* means "the yellow *amu*," specifically "chipmunk," and *amu-hwaa'a* means "the *amu* who feels like fighting," specifically "badger." This sort of thing is familiar to any student of southwestern Indian languages. For example, the Yuman word for dog, *hat*, apparently means "domestic animal." Under aboriginal conditions this did not often mean anything else but dog, so there was no conflict of meaning. Among the modern Yuma, however, this term began to be applied to "horse" only. Similarly, among the Hopi *sipala* was once a general term for fruit but later meant specifically "peach."

There are several techniques by which a root can be modified (Table 2.4). An additional element may be added in front (prefix) or back (suffix), or it may be tucked into the middle of the root itself (infix). The stressed vowel of the root may be changed (ablaut), or the root itself may be repeated (reduplication).

The Havasupai terms given in this chapter—and elsewhere throughout the book—should be considered illustrative only.*

---

* Whiting felt that much more work was needed on Havasupai linguistics. During his field work he made forty 78-rpm records, which are now in the possession of the editors of this book. Unfortunately, these recordings are not very useable without further technical processing.

3. Getting Enough to Eat

Many of the foods which were important in the diet of other aboriginal peoples in the Southwest were also available to the Havasupai. Mesquite, the prime staple among the Pima, could be found near the village. Mescal, which was so important to the Apache and Yavapai, grew along the canyon rims. Pinyon nuts, the prime staple of the natives of the Great Basin, were found along the South Rim of the Grand Canyon. Indian Rice Grass, which was of considerable importance to the Hopi at one time in their history, was also known to the Havasupai. In practice, however, many of these forms were relatively scarce in the area and, therefore, the Havasupai depended upon a variety of food staples, rather than upon one major item.

The basic protein needs were met with both plant and animal foods. Beans, sunflower, blazing star, and—above all— pinyon nuts, were relished for their fats and protein values. Meat was obtained from a number of large game animals, such as deer, pronghorn antelope, and bighorn sheep, as well as from a variety of smaller animals.

The chief source of starches in the Havasupai diet came from wild and domesticated grains. Wild tubers, roots and the like, did not seem to play any role in the native starch supply. The little, wild potato found in the Hopi country was absent. Apart from cultivated corn, the supply of starch foods came from numerous wild grasses and the seeds of wild amaranth, pigweed, mustards, and similar inconspicuous species.

The relative importance of agriculture is difficult to estimate. It most certainly varied greatly from family to family, as well as from year to year. In seasons in which there was an abundance of easily harvested wild seeds, agricultural produce was neglected or stored against future need. When agricultural products were curtailed through frost, flood, or poor growing season, there was a greater emphasis upon wild food supplies. When both failed, as sometimes happened, individual families often went to live with their more fortunate friends among the neighboring Hopi or Walapai. Although it was essential for each Havasupai family to have some agricultural land, no family could survive without gathering a considerable amount of wild food products. The people were, on the average, about equally dependent upon wild and domestic food resources.

By contrast, the Hopi obtained less than a third of their starch supply from wild foods. The intensity of their agriculture made them individually and collectively dependent upon a large and successful harvest. Hopi agriculture permitted concentration of the population in permanent villages and development of a complex social organization, an elaborate ritual, and an esthetically rich material culture. They were, however, completely dependent upon their agricultural economy. Hopi agriculture was a form of slavery against which the Havasupai were rebellious and to which they were only partially subject.

AGRICULTURE

In the bottom of Cataract Canyon between the great spring and the first falls there is a relatively level area not over three miles long and a quarter-mile wide. Here the Havasupai have practiced agriculture for centuries. Although the irregular canyon floor may contain five hundred acres, much of this area is taken up with talus slopes and rocky hills. The amount of land which could possibly be brought under cultivation probably never exceeded two hundred acres (Hoover 1929). For many years the river flowed near the level of the fields. Light dams of earth and brush were used to force small amounts of water into irrigation ditches at various points. Since about 1900, the river has been cutting down into this relatively level land, so that casual irrigation has become increasingly difficult. In 1920, the government assisted the Indians in developing a new irrigation system which provided for two main ditches, one on each side of the river. Water was forced into the ditches by small dams. This system of irrigation provided far more water than was needed, so that there was no need for an elaborate set of regulations to control the use of the water. Individuals took what water they needed by directing it to their fields through a network of secondary ditches. Because the sandy soil was easily eroded, the main ditches had to be repaired constantly; the secondary ditches were repaired as needed.

Because of the irregularities of the land, the plots tended to be irregular in shape. When new land was cleared, small brush was pulled and burned, and large trees were girdled and cut down or burned. Girdling may have been a relatively new technique, since Spier (1928) specifically denied its use. The soil within the fields was made up of travertine and was therefore fertile and easily worked.

The agricultural tools used by the early Havasupai were limited. Francisco Garcés, writing about his visit in 1776, said they obtained "hatchets, dibbles, and hoes" from the Hopi (Coues 1900). Cushing (1882) described a digging stick of juniper which had a side branch used as a foot rest. He also spoke of picks made of wood, bone, horn, or iron. According to Spier (1928), they used a broad-bladed digging stick, which served much the same purpose as a hoe or shovel. He further stated that the shoulder blade of a horse (never a deer) was also used for scraping out weeds. These agricultural tools were also used in building the irrigation ditches (D.I.). By 1941 these tools had virtually disappeared and had been replaced by commercial tools.

A cultivated Havasupai field. Note the earthen dam and channels for water, diverted from Cataract Creek. The high cliffs surrounding the fields limit the amount of direct sunshine during the growing season. Photo from A. F. Whiting's files, 1941.

In the spring the land was cleared of last year's debris and made ready for planting. Table 3.1 shows the variety of food plants cultivated by the Havasupai. In April or May the land was irrigated by flooding one section after another. About two days after the flooding, corn was planted (Spier 1928) after soaking the seeds overnight. The rows were marked out roughly with the foot, and the planter then used a digging stick to loosen the soil to a depth of about eight inches, which left a hole two to three inches deep. Before placing the first seed in the hole, the planter said a prayer (Spier 1928). He then dropped six to ten kernels into the hole. Chewing an additional kernel, he blew it toward two white marks on the canyon wall which represented the two original ancestral ears presented to the Havasupai by the mythical twin heroes. (For a fuller discussion of Havasupai beliefs, see Smithson and Euler [1964]). The first hole was filled with soil and, after two short strides forward, a second hole was dug and planted without further ceremony. The more recent use of modern plows and hoes has not changed this procedure. Planting was often a family occupation. Several men might plant one field, following the leader's spacing (Spier 1928). Observations in 1941 confirmed the report published by Spier (1928).

Little attention was given to the crops as they were growing. When the corn was six to eighteen inches high, the farmer loosened the soil around each group of plants and pulled it into hills around their base. This process, called *cepukaka*, helped to keep the corn from blowing over. The crop was then irrigated a second time.

During the growing season some attempt was made to protect the growing crops from rodents and other animals by fencing the plots. In addition, dogs and pet hawks were sometimes stationed in the fields to scare rodents and birds away (E.U., M.T.), and sometimes traps were set near the fields. When tassels appeared on the corn, two to two and one-half months later, the fields were given a third and last watering (Spier 1928). Corn ripened in two to four months, depending

TABLE 3.1
Cultivated Food Plants

Scientific Name	Common Name
Aboriginal	
Cucurbita moschata	squash, pumpkin
Gossypium spp.	cotton
Helianthus annuus	Hopi sunflower
Laginaria vulgaris	gourd
Phaseolus acutifolius	tepary bean
Phaseolus lunatus	lima bean
Phaseolus vulgaris	kidney bean
Proboscidea spp.	devil's claw
Zea mays	corn
Introduced by Euro-Americans	
Carya illinoensis	pecan
Citrullus vulgaris	watermelon
Cucumis melo	cantaloupe
Ficus carica	fig
Malus sylvestris	apple
Medicago sativa	alfalfa
Prunus armeniaca	apricot
Prunus persica	peach
Prunus spp.	plums
Pyrus communis	pear
Vigna sinensis	black-eyed pea
Introduced, but Rejected or Little Used	
Allium spp.	onions
Capsicum annuum	chili
Ipomoea batatas	sweet potato
Lycopersicon esculentum	tomato
Pisum sativum	pea
Prunus amygdalus	almond
Prunus spp.	cherries
Triticum aestivum	wheat

upon the variety and the season. Blue corn, which has the shortest season, was planted early and was available for eating in early June. The main harvest of longer-season white corn ripened in August and September (Spier 1928).

In addition to several varieties of corn the Havasupai raised beans, squash and sunflowers, as well as small amounts of gourds and cotton. At harvest time seeds were selected for superior form and yield in corn and beans, and for sweetness in squash and sunflowers. Because the Havasupai had repeatedly lost their planting seeds through floods and other emergencies, and had been forced to restock from their neighbors, the ancestral types of many plants have disappeared. Corn and beans were borrowed from both the Hopi and the Walapai. The varieties obtained from the Walapai often came originally from the Mohave, but in many cases the Havasupai were merely borrowing back a Hopi variety they had lent to the Walapai in some previous season.

While there was a general attempt to keep the varieties separate, the close proximity of the fields, necessitated by the topography, resulted in a constant mixing of varieties. The different varieties were identifiable, however, because they tended to mature at different times.

Beans were raised in small quantities, often in the same fields as corn. They were harvested in the fall. The dried bean pods were rubbed between the palms of the hands above a shallow basket tray. As they separated, the beans and the pods were allowed to fall into the tray within which they were then winnowed. Sunflowers were also raised in the corn fields, often as a row along the edge of the field. The heads were gathered, allowed to dry, and threshed; the seeds were then stored for later use. The sunflower types raised in 1941 were apparent mixtures of wild forms and were not significantly different from the well-known Hopi type. Squash, too, was planted in the fields with or adjacent to corn. After the corn was removed, the squash might be left in the fields to ripen. The "old" types growing in 1941 seemed to be essentially similar to those raised by the Hopi.

Cotton, which was used only for wicks for the strike-a-light, seems to have been a very minor crop. Seeds were not saved but were obtained as needed from the Hopi. Gourd seeds were also obtained from the Hopi. Gourds were raised by the medicine men for rattles or were used as water containers.

Devil's claw, used in basketry, was introduced into the native agriculture at an early date. Of the two varieties recognized in 1941, the older had long since established itself as a weed appearing in gardens. Devil's claw, like other useful weeds (such as amaranth), was allowed to grow wherever it came up as long as it did not materially hinder the planted crop. A second variety of more recent introduction had to be planted.

Melons, watermelons, and orchard trees became available to the Havasupai after the arrival of the Spanish. Many of these were received from the Hopi, who had obtained them from the Spanish. In 1941 watermelons, cantaloupes, and several other melons were very popular. By this time new strains of the old staple crops, such as black-eyed peas and new varieties of corn, had also found their way into Havasupai agriculture through commercial and native channels.

Orchard crops were widely accepted. Peaches were introduced some time before 1876. There has been a widespread story among local Arizonans that they were introduced by John D. Lee, an ex–Indian agent and refugee Mormon. A later review of the historical data (Whiting 1948) showed the improbability of this story. In view of the fact that they use the Hopi name for this fruit, it seems probable that the Havasupai obtained peaches from that tribe. In 1941 apples and figs were very popular. Almond, apricot, pear, plum, and (recently) cherry trees, as well as grape vines, were occasionally seen. Many of these had been introduced by the government agents. Pecans, for example, grew chiefly upon government land, although a few families had trees of their own.

Vegetables were not as popular among the Havasupai as they were among the Hopi. Chili and onions were not seen in 1941, though they had been referred to by early visitors, and peas

---

* For further discussion of devil's claw domestication and the Havasupai, see Nabhan et al. (1981).

and tomatoes were rarely raised. The resident government farmer complained bitterly, saying that the Havasupai would not irrigate frequently enough to produce vegetables. In fact, although the Havasupai had abundant water resources, by 1941 they had little more than duplicated the effects of flood-water irrigation as practiced by the Hopi. Even with instruction and examples by resident farmer-agents, these procedures did not change much. The Havasupai indifference toward agriculture was in marked contrast to the Hopi, particularly those who were raising crops under irrigation at Moenkopi.

The appearance of horses and cattle placed a premium upon adequate pasturage, particularly at certain seasons of the year. In 1941 a considerable portion of the irrigated farm land was devoted to alfalfa, and the amount of land available for other crops was, thus, reduced.

HUNTING

Even as late as 1941, the Havasupai were still not farmers in the sense that the Hopi and other Pueblo Indians were. There was little pride or interest in work on the farms: the fields were not well tended, the interest in crop varieties was incidental, there was no enthusiasm for new crops. Agricultural resources, though limited, were not exploited to their full potential, and it is clearly evident that the Havasupai thought of their agriculture as something incidental, a supplement to a hunting-gathering way of life.

Equipment

Bows and arrows were of primary importance in hunting large game (see Table 3.2). The animals and plants used in making the bow and arrow and other hunting equipment are shown in Table 3.3. Children's toy bows were D-shaped and quite simple. Large, stronger bows were made of ash or similar woods. The finest bow wood was obtained from an unidentified tree, possibly the mulberry. Suitable trees were kept carefully trimmed of side branches for several years before the wood for

TABLE 3.2
Hunting Equipment

English Term	Havasupai Term
Bow	*hapuu*
Arrow	*apa'a*
Sinew	*mesma'a*
Sinew-backed bow	*mesma'a*
Sinew bow string	*mesma-hapacinakia*
Wrist guard	*salame* (cf. hand, *sal*)
Arrow-shaft straightener	*muqwapacia metemiya*
Arrow-shaft smoother	*patamalia*
Rills	*apasa'uika*
Quiver	*nyipuwa*
Arrow feather	*ipahuu'u*
Arrow head	*kwaiyal*
Notch at end of arrow	*ipacitaova*
Deer calculus	*qwakiyala*
Bullet	*mipa'a* or *apa'a*
Rifle	*kweka*

a bow was cut. The very best bows were sinew backed. Such bows required much time and effort to make and were greatly prized.

The bow was made, according to P.B., in the following manner:

A branch is selected. This may be slightly curved naturally, but should be without sharp angles or side branches. This branch is then partially dried for two days. The maker then takes a hatchet and roughs out the bow. Approximately half of the wood is removed from the face of the bow, except that portion at the center which is used for the grip. The back of the bow is somewhat flattened. The wood is finished by scraping with a knife. If the original piece was curved, the concave side becomes the back of the bow. After the bow is carved out, the wood is rubbed with the lard of bighorn sheep and placed in the sun for half an hour. It is then heated for twenty minutes over the edge of the fire, but not in the flame. The

TABLE 3.3
Animals and Plants Used in Making Hunting Equipment

Scientific Name	Common Name
Animals	
Aquila chrysaetos	Golden eagle
Buteo jamaicensis	Red-tailed Hawk
Buteo regalis	Ferruginous Hawk
Buteo lagopus	Rough-legged Hawk
Circus cyaneus	Northern Harrier
Falco mexicanus	Prairie Falcon
Felis concolor	mountain lion
Odocoileus hemionus	fawns (mule deer)
Ovis canadensis	bighorn sheep
Plants	
Amelanchier utahensis	serviceberry
Fendlera rupicola	saxifrage
Fraxinus pennsylvanica	ash
Mortonia scabrella	----------
Morus microphylla	mulberry
Penstemon pachyphyllus	blue beardtongue
Phragmites communis	reed

bowmaker next grips one end of the bow with one hand and the middle of the bow with the other, in such a manner that he is facing the inside of the bow. The portion between his two hands is then carefully bent over the knee. This is then repeated on the other side. The bow is now strung with sinew. One end is firmly attached to the top end of the bow. The other end is wrapped four or five times around the bow and fastened with two or three half-hitches. A short piece is left hanging. This end is always held down when shooting and is the end which is loosened when the bow is not in use.

The bow string was of twisted sinew and at least three lengths were needed. The ends of the added lengths were inserted, without knots, at intervals, with ends overlapping slightly, and then the whole string was twisted. Bow strings of rich men had an extra length of buckskin attached to the lower end. When not in use, the strings of the sinew-backed bows were loosened slightly, but because of the reversed curves of the bow and the attached sinew, they were never completely relaxed.

The left wrist of the archer was protected by a leather wrist guard. For large game, heavy wooden arrows were used, often with large stone points or, in more recent times, metal points. These arrowheads were set with gum made from lac, which was received in trade from the Mohave.* These arrows were made of hard woods, such as serviceberry, *Fendlera*, or *Mortonia*. Since most arrows were from shrubs rather than trees, it must have been difficult to find a supply of straight branches. Arrow-shaft straighteners, made of bighorn sheep shoulder blades with holes in them, must have been essential. Smoothers of channeled stone were also used. Rills were cut in these arrowshafts with a special implement.

Feathers for arrows were obtained from birds raised in cages or tied by one leg to a tree. The secondary feathers of ferruginous or rough-legged hawks were particularly desired. Birds with white tails were especially chosen, because the tail feathers were used in religious rituals. Other birds, whose feathers were used but which were not raised, included the Red-tailed Hawk, Northern Harrier, Prairie Falcon, and Eagle.

Arrows were carried in a skin quiver hung over the shoulder. Rich men had quivers made from the hides of fawns or young bighorn sheep.

In 1941 rifles and ammunition purchased at a store or through mail-order houses were in universal use. The old word for arrow is now applied to bullet as well.

Hunting equipment for small game included the same bows which were used for larger game, but the arrows, usually made

---

* Robert C. Euler (personal communication, 1983) stated that lac could also have been obtained from Walapai along the Big Sandy. To his knowledge it has not been observed on *Larrea* growing in the lower reaches of Havasupai country.

of reed with hardwood foreshafts, were lighter in weight. The shaft was prepared from semi-dry (mature) reeds. The surface was peeled off to make the shaft smooth, and the top, or small end, was cut close above the node with a sharp "V" for the nock. The shafts were straightened after they had been heated in hot ashes (Jackson). This procedure had to be done in secret where no one could see, or the arrow would be likely to break (E.U.). Paint and feathers were subsequently applied to the base of the shaft. The foreshaft was usually of pointed wood. Occasionally, for special purposes, a stone or iron point was used, and sometimes a simple foreshaft with a corncob bunt was used to stun small game. These light arrows were used for rabbits, birds, and small animals, never for large game or in war.

Special hunting sticks or clubs were used for certain animals. A pole was notched and roughened on one end so that it would catch in the fur of rabbits hiding in hollow logs. In 1941, the hunter was more likely to chop the log open with a steel axe. Sticks, roughly the size of baseball bats but tapering more toward the end, were used to club a treed porcupine or bobcat or to dispatch a coyote or fox trapped by deep snows. A badger was likewise killed by hitting it on the head. A rabbit, however, was never clubbed, but was killed by pinching and rupturing the heart while the hunter held the animal captive. The throwing stick or boomerang used by the Hopi was not used, although the Havasupai were familiar with it, and one of their own myths tells how a hero used it to take off the heads of his enemies.

Rabbits and birds were sometimes felled with a well-thrown stone. A sling made of a patch of leather with buckskin thongs was used for rabbits. Simple death-fall traps were placed along rodent runways. A myth tells how Fox-man used a large death-fall to trap a wide variety of animals. One man described a "pea-shooter" made of *Baccharis* with which it was possible to kill birds.

TABLE 3.4
Animals Used for Food

Scientific Name	Common Name
Anatidae	ducks
Antilocapra americana	pronghorn
*Bos taurus	cattle
*#Capra hircus	goat
Cervus canadensis	elk
*Equus caballus	horse
*Equus hemionus	burro
Erethizon dorsatum	porcupine
Felis concolor	mountain lion
*Gallus gallus	chicken
Lepus californicus	jackrabbit
Lophortyx gambelii	Gambel's Quail
Lynx rufus	bobcat
Meleagris gallopavo	Turkey
Neotoma spp.	woodrats
Odocoileus hemionus	mule deer
*#Ovis aries	sheep
Ovis canadensis	bighorn sheep
Spermophilus variegatus	rock squirrel
Sylvilagus audubonii	cottontail rabbit
Taxidea taxus	badger

*Introduced
#Not retained

Hunting Techniques and Distribution of Meat

The Havasupai made use of both large and small animals for food (see Table 3.4). Pronghorn used to be abundant in the lightly forested open plains south of the Grand Canyon. After 1890 they began to decrease in numbers, and by 1907 they had virtually disappeared from the area.* A hunter, disguised under a stuffed pronghorn head, his body painted white, held

---

* In 1984 pronghorn were once again seen south of the Grand Canyon. This increase may be due to the fact that the area is in a national park, where the animals are protected.

two sticks in his hands to imitate the forelegs of the creatures. Placing himself where a herd could see him, he would imitate the creature's habits of shaking the head and playing with the bushes. This attracted their attention, and their curiosity did the rest. They came to him! The hunter had a strong bow and heavy wooden arrows with stone points concealed under one arm and, when the animals were close enough, quick action would bring down one or several of them.

Bighorn sheep were exceedingly rare in 1941, and were no longer hunted. However, they were once quite abundant in the Grand Canyon and were frequently found in the vicinity of the village in Cataract Canyon. Although sheep were occasionally shot near the village, they were usually hunted in the canyon above the village to the south and within the Grand Canyon area to the east. Sometimes hunters wore a disguise consisting of stuffed ewe's head with horns of stuffed buckskin and buckskin hide colored with ashes. More often the sheep were driven past places where other hunters waited in ambush, or they might be driven directly over the cliffs. Brush and grass were sometimes set on fire to aid in these drives.

Deer were found in the wooded areas to the east and west of Cataract Canyon along the South Rim of the Grand Canyon and in the mountains across the open plains to the south. Formerly they were of less importance than pronghorn and bighorn sheep, but with the disappearance of these important game animals the deer took on increasing significance. Deer were still hunted to some extent in 1941, but they were not a significant source of meat. Elk were occasionally found near the San Francisco Peaks, but they were never an important element in the native diet.

Many of the hunting habits recently associated with deer formerly applied to pronghorn and bighorn sheep. A hunter, for example, should not have intercourse with his wife for several days before going hunting. If he did, the animal would readily catch the scent of the pursuer, the hunter would not be able to see any game, or the animals would not be fat. During a hunt a man could not eat meat, and should eat only corn and mescal. His face was painted red, though this may have been, at least in part, a protection against sunburn. There were certain magical procedures involving the burning of deer droppings and the marking of the faces of the hunters with the ashes. The chief was supposed to make prayers to the sun for a large hunting party. These techniques were employed primarily for large hunting parties and may have been particularly important when game was scarce. Individual luck could be acquired in dreams or the hunter might carry a calculus from the paunch of a deer.

Hunters attracted deer with a sound "like a baby deer" made with a folded leaf of the blue penstemon. It was placed in the mouth like a harmonica, so that the edge of the leaf was next to the teeth, and air could be sucked in around it. Disguises similar to those described for antelope and mountain sheep were also used when hunting deer. Dogs were used to track wounded deer over hard ground, but never for locating fresh game.

Special care had to be taken with pronghorn meat, for it was thought that the person who swallowed pronghorn hair would surely die. The liver might be eaten raw, and at times the undigested contents of the stomach of deer might be eaten. Strips of meat were cooked on skewers over the campfire. Fresh meat which was not to be eaten immediately was cut into strips and dried in the sun. It might be pounded between rocks several times during this drying process to insure thorough drying. Such jerked meat would keep indefinitely.

Within the historic period pronghorn were hunted by groups of men on horseback with bow and arrow. A man with a poor or tired horse might ask another hunter on a fresh horse to get an animal for him. Similar procedures were also applied to deer. The man who actually killed the animal retained the hide and sinew, both of which had economic value. Meat, however, had to be divided among the members of the party. A boy did not eat any of the meat from the first deer he killed. When a hunting party returned to the village the entire group might eat together. This method of distribution had an important aspect. Meat could be preserved only with difficulty, and fresh meat had to be consumed within a fairly short time. Thus, a series of minor hunting parties could keep the village in fresh meat over a long period of time, whereas a single concentrated period of hunting—such as the present restricted hunting season—would have, at best, left the camp with plenty of jerky but without fresh meat for long period of time.*

Within recent times the use of domestic animals, such as horses and cows, has followed this old pattern. Mrs. B. J. described the events which followed the killing of a horse for food. Half the animal was to be cooked. The chief announced a feast, and all the village helped eat the fresh meat. The roasted bones were pounded and the exposed marrow also eaten. The remaining half of the animal was jerked.

The Havasupai pattern of distributing meat throughout the group has been amply attested to both from the early historic sources (Garcés in 1776) and from more modern accounts. In all probability men hunted in rotation and the resulting reciprocal exchanges of fresh meat must have balanced, though there were undoubtedly some more or less dependent units which could not reciprocate. Since the valuable hides and sinew of the slain animal were always the property of the man who killed it, the pattern could not have created much hardship or economic dislocation.

Under conditions in 1941, the hunting of sizable game was restricted to a very short period of time and, with cattle very irregularly distributed throughout the tribe, the feeling of obligation to share with everyone was decreasing. In practice, fresh meat was still occasionally distributed throughout the village,

---

* A 1983 Supreme Court ruling indicated that Indians could hunt at any time they chose on their own reservations. See "State case on Indians set back," *Arizona Republic*, June 15, 1983.

TABLE 3.5
Animals With Food Taboos

Scientific Name	Common Name
Aguila chrysaetos	Golden Eagle
Anura	frog
Bassariscus astutus	ringtail
Canis latrans	coyote
Canis lupus	wolf
Felis concolor	mountain lion
Lynx rufus	bobcat
Osteichthyes	fish
Sauromalus obesus	chuckwalla
Urocyon cinereoargenteus	gray fox

but there was a definite sense of money value and more and more meat was traded or sold for cash.

Small game has always been abundant in this area and it is probable that in aboriginal times a considerable portion of the native meat supply was obtained from this source. Porcupines, bobcats, rabbits, and turkeys were locally abundant and frequently hunted. Smaller game, such as quail, doves, small rodents—particularly rock squirrels (tree squirrels were not eaten)—and woodrats were frequently trapped or hunted, especially by boys.

Certain food restrictions had to be observed; animals with food taboos are shown in Table 3.5. Parents of young children never ate the meat of mountain lion or bobcat, nor would they eat the meat of other animals that had been killed by, or even touched by, a mountain lion, bobcat, fox, coyote, wolf, ringtail cat, or eagle. To have broken this taboo might have caused a fatal illness in the child. Older people and people without children could eat these forbidden meats without danger. Chuckwallas, which were eaten by the Walapai and the Paiute, were avoided by the Havasupai, as were frogs, because killing these animals would have caused destructive storms. Fish were not eaten. There was little opportunity to obtain fish, and besides "they smell."

Rabbit drives were made, but even when all the available men and boys were employed, there were not enough people to surround an area as was done by the Hopi. Nets, such as those made of Indian hemp (dogbane) by the Walapai, were not used (Spier 1928). Rabbits were hunted in the snow, when they could be tracked with ease. Coyotes, and foxes were likewise hunted when deep snow hampered their movements.

Many game animals, such as mountain lions, bobcats, badgers, and porcupines, were often baked in an earth oven by men who were on camping or hunting trips. If they were brought back to camp they might be boiled by the women, but such meat was rarely jerked. A porcupine, however, required special treatment before it could be transported. The animal was placed on a fire as close as possible to the point at which it had been killed. This procedure effectively removed the quills and enabled the hunter to carry it home with some degree of comfort. Birds, such as quail, ducks, turkeys, and especially doves, were caught and cooked in earth ovens by small hunting parties, although they were not popular back in camp. Rabbits, woodrats, and rock squirrels were likewise baked in an earth oven in the field, and they often found their way into the boiling vessels in camp.

Quail seem to have had some special significance for the Havasupai. They were formerly abundant in the valley, but for some reason were unpopular as a source of food except among youngsters on a hunting-picnic in the nearby brush. The eggs of quail were eaten. They could be found during the nesting season under the bushes in the vicinity of the village.

Domestic Animals

Domesticated animals have never played an important part in Havasupai food economy. Sheep were not adapted to the rough mountainous terrain. Goats, though once introduced, were not adopted because of their constant ravaging of the meager gardens and also probably because of the lack of any really adequate pasture near the village. Goat herding in the valley certainly did not fit the general pattern of Havasupai life.

Chickens were first obtained from the Hopi many years ago and have been regarded with many of the old attitudes formerly expressed towards quail. They were restrained only during the period when they might do damage to the growing crops. At all other times they wandered about the valley, much as the quail formerly did. Eggs were collected primarily during the same season of the year when quail eggs used to be eaten. Like quail, the adult birds were eaten only upon rare occasions; chicken dinners at the school were very unpopular among the Indian pupils.

Horses, mules, and burros, though occasionally eaten, were never raised primarily as food. By 1941 the Havasupai were raising a few cattle.

GATHERING

It is important to note that most of the wild plants used for food were weed species. In 1941 the Havasupai often found it difficult to locate even an isolated specimen of many of the old staple wild food plants. Under the conditions which prevailed a century ago, these weed species were undoubtedly more abundant.

Collecting Wild Seeds

Many different seeds and nuts were gathered by Havasupai women for food (Table 3.6). In general there were two methods of collecting seeds. The first and more direct method consisted of knocking the seeds from the plant directly into a small collecting basket which was held in the left hand. When the basket was full, the contents were tossed over the shoulder into a big, conical carrying basket which rested on the back, supported by a carrying strap over the forehead or chest. When these baskets were nearly full, they were in turn dumped into a skin sack left at some central point in the collecting area. After working for most of the day, a woman might fill several such sacks. When horses were available, the men would ride out in the evening to pick up these sacks and carry them back to the camp. Before horses were available, these sacks had to be

TABLE 3.6
Wild Seeds and Nuts Used for Food

Scientific Name	Common Name
Acacia greggii	catclaw
Amaranthus hybridus	amaranth
Artemisia carruthii	wormwood, sagebrush
Artemisia pacifica	wormwood, sagebrush
Capsella bursa-pastoris	shepherds purse
Chenopodium spp.	goosefoot, pigweeds
Chenopodium fremontii	goosefoot, pigweed
Descurainia spp.	tansy mustards
Echinocactus spp.	barrel cacti
Gaillardia pinnatifida	blanket flower
Gilia sinuata	gilia
Helianthus petiolaris	wild sunflower
Juglans major	walnut
Koeleria cristata	June grass
Lepidium lasiocarpum	peppergrass
Mentzelia albicaulis	blazing star
Oryzopsis hymenoides	Indian millet
Pinus edulis	pinyon
Pinus ponderosa	yellow pine
Plantago purshii	Indian wheat
Poa fendleriana	mutton grass
Thlaspi montanum	wild candytuft

carried into camp on the backs of the women themselves. In the second method of collecting, the heads of grasses or other plants were gathered before the seeds were ready to fall. In this highly efficient method handfuls of fruiting heads, sometimes tied into bundles, were put into the carrying basket.

Different plants required different treatment to separate the seeds from the stems and chaff. For example, the bunched heads of mutton grass were steamed in an earth oven lined with flat rocks. Some pounded these lightly with a stone mano or muller to force the seeds out from between the bracts of the chaff. Others set a basket into the ground and tramped on the heads. After the heads of pigweed or goosefoot were collected and dried, the seeds were separated by rubbing them between

the palms of the hands over a basket. They were then winnowed by repeatedly tossing the contents of the basket into the
air. At times, however, these seeds might be knocked from the
ripe heads directly into the collecting basket. Catclaw pods
were gathered from the tree, spread on a blanket, and threshed
with a stick. Perhaps one-half of the crop was stored in a
pouch of deerskin or a sack made from a Navajo blanket, while
the remainder was used immediately.

The fruiting heads of Indian millet were large and contained
many long, thin, dry stems. In addition, at the base of each
seed was a tuft of hair. The seeds were, therefore, difficult to
collect and clean for use. The Havasupai collected the heads
and piled them upon a large flat stone. When they were dry,
the entire pile was set on fire and poked occasionally to insure
complete burning. When the fire died down, most of the fine
stems and hairs at the base of the seeds were gone, and the
seeds had been toasted so that no further parching was necessary. The seeds were then separated from the remaining debris
by placing them in a large, conical carrying basket that had
been set in a hole in the ground. They were then trampled with
bare feet, winnowed in the usual fashion, and stored for future
use.

Processing and Storage of Plant Foods

Under aboriginal conditions it was essential that most foods
which were to be kept for any period of time be dried to
prevent spoiling (see Table 3.7). In addition, since much of the
food produced in Cataract Canyon eventually had to be packed
out to the Plateau, it was desirable to have light, concentrated
food products. Drying techniques were, therefore, important.
The older method of drying food on the ground necessitated
protecting it from animals by setting traps, building repulsive
smudges of dung, and keeping an almost constant eye for
rodents. In 1941 the firm, flat roofs of the relatively permanent
ramadas in the village offered reasonably safe places on which
to dry the food.

TABLE 3.7
Food Plants That Were Dried and Stored

Scientific Name	Common Name
Agave utahensis	mescal
*Cucumis melo	melons
*Cucurbita moschata	squash (pumpkin)
*Ficus carica	fig
Lycium pallidum	desert thorn
Nolina bigelovii	bear grass
Opuntia phaeacantha	prickly pear
Prosopis juliflora	mesquite
*Prunus persica	peach
Rhus trilobata	squawbush
Vitis arizonica	wild grape
Yucca baccata	broad-leaved yucca
*Zea mays	corn

*Introduced or domesticated species

The necessity for dry, light foods that could be stored in a small space and transported for long distances dictated that corn be shelled from the cob. Ripe squash was taken to the house and the heavy rind hacked off with a knife. A hole was cut in one end of the squash so that the seeds could be removed, and the flesh was then cut spirally in such a manner that it was reduced to a single, long strand, an inch or so wide and a quarter to half an inch thick. The strand was allowed to dry and then wrapped into a bundle, like rope. These "hanks" of squash could be hung in the house or in a storage cist for future use. When wanted, portions were cut off and boiled. This technique was still in use in 1941. Melons were cut in two, the seeds removed, and the resulting hemispheric shells (fruit and rind) flattened and dried. The Hopi prepare both squash and melons in the same manner but use considerably more care and obtain a far neater product than do the Havasupai.

Many fresh food products were reduced to a flat mat. These mats not only preserved the materials, they also provided a convenient unit for transportation and trade. Some of these mats could be made without much difficulty. The preparation of mescal mats, however, required considerable effort. In early spring, children were excused from school and groups of families moved up into the Esplanade and the upper branches of Cataract Canyon, where the century plants were abundant. Some people preferred to carry the mescal some distance back to the village or up onto the Plateau where firewood was more readily abundant. In any case, the men gathered firewood and prepared the roasting pit,* which was usually dug in sandy soil, but never in gravel, which would allow too much steam to escape. The collection of the mescal heads was primarily the task of the women. A chisel-pointed stick of buckthorn two to three feet long was inserted at the base of the plant. The end of the stick was pounded with a rock to loosen the head of spiny leaves. The loose head was then trimmed of its outer leaves and the spiny portions of the leaves that had not yet unfolded. After the heads had been trimmed, they were pulled off, and the women would bring them back to the fire-pit area. Several trips might be necessary. Each family had a separate pile, often with as many as forty heads in each pile.

A pit, four to six feet in diameter and about four feet deep, was dug and then filled with brush and wood to a height of about four feet above the ground. Over this pile was spread a thick layer of stones, larger ones first and then smaller ones. The fire was ignited by any person who was born in the summer. If the fire was ignited by a person born during the winter the mescal would not cook completely. In an hour or two, when the fire had burned down, the men would take poles or large rocks and attempt to tamp down the hot rocks into an even surface. Breaks in this rocky surface were filled with fresh gravel, and the rocks were then covered with a "grass" previously collected by the women. The mescal heads were now

---

* Robert C. Euler, in a 1983 personal communication, indicated that the most abundant archaeological remains on the Esplanade are mescal pits, some as much as nine feet in diameter.

placed in the pit (each family was allotted a pie-shaped section). The pile was covered with more grass or, in more recent times, with a gunny sack, then covered with a layer of dirt at least six inches deep.

The mound had to be watched to make sure that a steam vent did not appear and allow the heat to escape. The people tending the mescal were not allowed to eat salt, or the resulting product would be bitter. Married people would sleep separately during this time. Corn was the only food eaten. No one would smoke and their faces were painted with red paint. The length of time required to cook the mescal varied from twelve to forty-eight hours. A sampling might be taken and, if the mescal was not ready, the pit was closed and covered again.

When the mescal was cooked, it was piled outside the pit. Thin slices from the core of the freshly baked heads were dried in the sun and were considered a delicacy. The cooked heads were mashed flat with stones and spread out on drying racks made of split stalks of bear grass, agave, or reeds tied together with twined yucca leaves or rawhide strips. If such a drying rack was not available, the mescal might be dried on a bed of Mormon tea twigs spread over the ground or on a smooth rock.

The mescal heads which were badly burned in the firing, together with the first head pounded, were boiled in water. This produced a thin, dark liquid which was painted over the top of the drying mescal mats. The mats were turned from time to time and, while still pliable, were folded into convenient widths for storage and transportation. A face paint was also prepared at this time. Stones from the pit that had become coated with mescal juice during the baking were placed in a jar of water to dissolve the juice. The resulting liquid was boiled until it thickened, and red hematite was added to thicken it further. This process produced a doughy mass which was worked into a ball for storage (Spier 1928). When paint was needed, scrapings from this ball were mixed with saliva and applied to the face with a yucca-fiber brush.

The fruits of the prickly pear were knocked off the cactus, rolled on the ground, and brushed to remove the spines. They were then slit open, the seeds were removed, and the remaining flesh was dried in the sun. Sometimes they were pounded into a cake for storage or trade.

Several varieties of old-world figs which grew in Cataract Canyon were picked from the tree, split open with the fingers and dried in the sun for storage. Those which had fallen from the tree might be picked up, ground on a metate, and mixed with water to form a thick paste. The paste was dried in the form of sheets, about six by twelve inches, and preserved for winter. When needed, portions were broken off and eaten.

The ripe fruits of the broad-leaved yucca were laid on a bed of dry sticks which were then burned. The blackened and partially cooked fruit was then removed with tongs and sprinkled with water. The flesh was separated from the burned rind and the seeds were ground or mashed on a metate and spread out to dry as a sheet or mat. The mat might be folded for storage. Bits of it were broken off from time to time and either eaten directly or boiled and the resulting liquid used as a drink.

Mesquite has dry, fleshy beans which were eaten directly or processed and stored. Processing entailed pounding the bean pods into a powder. A layer of this powder was sprinkled over mesquite seeds, which were used to form the base layer of a storage cake. Water was sprinkled over the first layer of powder, and then a second layer was added and moistened. This procedure continued until the cake was two to three inches thick. A piece of the stored cake was broken off and either eaten directly or first soaked in water. The inedible seeds which formed the base layer were spit out.

Peaches were an important element in the Havasupai diet in 1941. After they were gathered, frequently by shaking the tree and picking the fallen fruit off the ground, they were split open with the fingers, dried in the sun and then stored. There was no attempt to reduce them to mats.

The fresh berries of the squawbush were either made into a "lemonade" or they were dried in the sun and stored in sacks for future use. The berries of the desert thorn were used in the same fashion.

Prehistorically, it was essential to store food where it would be protected from rodents and other animals, as well as from raiding enemies. The Havasupai solved this problem by constructing small, often beehive-shaped, storage cists of stone and clay under low, overhanging ledges in the canyon walls. When these were filled, the entrance was tightly sealed with mud. These storage cists kept the food dry and safe from animals. They were located high above the level of flood waters and were hidden in unfrequented corners of neighboring canyons, often at some distance from the village. As the fear of hostile raiding parties decreased, they were built nearer the houses in the village, just above the level of possible flood waters.

With the establishment of permanent residence in the valley and with the subsequent changes in domestic architecture, these storage cists were gradually abandoned. By 1941 very few were still in use. By then, corn was stored on the cob, squash and melons were kept for long periods without being cut up and dried, and watermelons were kept and used for several months after the harvest was over. New techniques for processing and storing were also appearing. Through the school women were learning to cook and can fruits and to make jams and jellies. In addition, fresh meat could be purchased through stores at Grand Canyon Village, and canned goods and other commercial products were finding a place in the native diet.

Fresh Spring Greens and Other Minor Food Resources

Greens, particularly desert plume, were eaten in the spring when for a short time they were an important, though minor, food (see Table 3.8). Havasupai custom dictated that only the leaves should be cut. Amaranth, which provided both greens and seeds, often grew in abandoned or harvested garden plots. When men were out on a hunt and badly in need of food, they

TABLE 3.8
Spring Greens and Other Minor Foods

Scientific Name	Common Name
Spring Greens	
Amaranthus hybridus	amaranth
Cirsium spp.	thistles
Eriogonum inflatum	desert trumpet
Rorippa nasturtium-aquaticum	watercress
Rumex crispus	wild rhubarb
Stanleya pinnata	desert plume
Other Foods	
Aloisia wrightii	wright lippa
Carya illinoensis	pecan
Ephedra viridis	mormon tea
Juglans rupestris major	wild walnut
Juniperus osteosperma	juniper
Pinus edulis	pinyon
Pinus ponderosa	ponderosa, yellow pine
Populus fremontii	cottonwood
Prunus amygdalus	almond
Typha domingensis	cattail

*Introduced species

sometimes took the leaves of thistles, held them in the fire until the spines were burned off, and ate them. Watercress was introduced around 1910. Celery, which had also been introduced, grew wild along the river below the village. In this form it was hardly recognizable as the familiar vegetable found on Anglo tables. It was not used by Havasupai.

Pinyon trees grow luxuriantly on the South Rim of the Grand Canyon, but the nut crop is erratic and the nature of the forthcoming harvest was often a topic of incidental conversation among the Havasupai in much the same way that the weather is in other societies. In September the green cones were collected and heated over a fire to open them up so that the nuts could be removed. The major portion of the pinyon harvest came late in the season. In favorable years, the pinyon crop must have played an important part in Havasupai economy.

During the harvest families gathered and lived in those areas in which the crops were abundant. In 1941 pinyon nuts were a source of income, as they could be sold at Anglo stores throughout the area.

The nuts of the yellow pine were formerly collected for food, though they were never as popular nor as important as those of the pinyon. Wild walnuts grew some distance up Cataract Canyon from the village. They were occasionally eaten, as were the cultivated pecans. A few almond trees were also raised, but they were of little importance. Juniper berries were eaten in cases of extreme need, but they were resinous and caused digestive upsets if eaten in quantity.

A few plants were used for semi-medicinal teas. These plants were sometimes collected in bundles and dried for future use. By 1941, coffee and other commercial beverages had largely supplanted this old usage. The green berries of the cottonwood and the heads of the cattail were chewed like gum. These were used as they were available but were never stored.

4. A Havasupai Cookbook

Havasupai cooking was simple, although there was a considerable variation in the diet from season to season. There were times when the food supply was not adequate and people went hungry, but there were also periods of feasting and overabundance. While the Havasupai did not develop many specialized dishes or a complicated menu, their cooking lacked the dull uniformity of the more culturally advanced Hopi.

COOKING EQUIPMENT

Havasupai cooking equipment (Table 4.1), varied with the season. When the Havasupai lived in the valley near their fields or in fixed winter camps, items such as milling stones and fragile pottery would be used, but, when they went on their hunting and gathering expeditions, much of this kind of equipment had to be left behind. On these trips they were dependent upon small portable items of stone and relatively indestructible basketry. These were supplemented by equipment which could be improvised from local resources.

Some of the pottery used in the semi-permanent camps was made locally, but much of it was imported from the Hopi. In camps where pottery was not available the people used cooking vessels of basketry. They were carefully woven and made

TABLE 4.1
Utensils Used in Food Preparation

Utensil	Havasupai Term (traditional form)	Havasupai Term (usual 1941 form)
Pottery vessel	*hamat* (cf. *amat*, earth)	*hamat*
Carrying basket	*kathak*	*kathak*
Basketry tray (twined)	*katha'u'u* (cf. *ka'u'u*, coiled tray)	*katha'u'u*
Parching tray	*katha'u'ulai'a* (cf. *alai'a*, spoiled)	*katha'u'ulai'a*
Water jug	*sawa*	----------
Boiling basket	*kwetalomia* (cf. *ta'olka*, to boil)	*kwetioola*, metal pot
Deep basket	*thituya*	*kwa-thutiya*, tin cup
Horn spoon	*muqwa* (*amu'u'*, mountain sheep; *qwa'a*, horn)	*qwamkwa'a*, metal spoon
----------	----------	*kwaksapa*, "metal points," fork (cf. *sapa*, points)
Stone knife	*kwa*	*kwa*, metal knife, metal
Knife with wood handle	*akwica*	*akwica*
Knife, arrowhead	*kwaiyal* (cf. *kwainyace*, black obsidian)	*kwaiyal*
Mortar	*awi'kwetutia*	*awi'kwetutia*
Pestle	*va'ha'ca'a*	*va'ha'ca'a*
Milling stone (lower)	*taka* (cf. *-tava*, to grind)	*taka*
Milling stone (upper)	*va'ha'ca'a*	*va'ha'ca'a*
Gourd jug	(?)	(?)
Stirring rod	(?)	(?)
Tongs	(?)	(?)

A water-storage basket sealed with pinyon pitch. Photo from A. F. Whiting's files, 1941.

watertight by rubbing mush into cracks and by treating the outside with boiled mescal juice. The basket was filled with water, and hot stones were dropped into it to make the water boil.

Baskets were among the most useful pieces of cooking equipment. A very useful basket was a shallow, plate-like tray When this became old and stained it was used to parch various seeds. It was lined with mush or, in more recent time, stewed peaches to provide a protective coating so that the hot coals used in parching would not char the basket. Jug-shaped baskets and tall storage baskets for carrying and storing water were coated with pinyon pitch. These could not be used with hot water. With the exception of the carrying jug, most of these forms were abandoned when metal containers became available about 1880.

There were two types of grinding stones: mortars for pounding or rotary grinding, and flat rocks, or milling stones, for back-and-forth grinding. Natural or artificial holes in rocks near camping places were used for stone boiling and for grinding and pounding. Occasionally a hole would be found in a small, more or less portable boulder which could be transported to the semi-permanent camps. Rotary grinding was done with a hard rock pestle. The stone slabs for back-and-forth grinding were roughly rectangular. Large grinding stones (thirty by twenty inches) would be left in the more permanent camps while smaller ones (twenty-five by twelve inches) would be taken from camp to camp. The Havasupai grinding stones were made from a hard stone which, in contrast to those of the Hopi, did not leave grit in the meal. Such stones were difficult to obtain and were highly prized. The mano, or hand stone, with which the grinding was done varied in size from two to five inches by four to eight inches.

Before metal knives were available, chipped blades of flint and obsidian were used. An aboriginal knife described by informants consisted of a large blade set at right angles in the center of a handle made of pinyon. The stone blade was held in

A Havasupai woman grinding seeds.
Photo by Robert C. Euler, 1956.

Large spoons, made from the horns of bighorn sheep, were used in cooking and baking. Photo from A. F. Whiting's files, 1941.

place with pitch and by lashings. This aboriginal knife was hafted expressly for the cutting of *Agave*. Iron blades have been used by the Havasupai for some time. P.B. described the following procedure in making a metal knife: "Take a section of pinyon wood about the size of my arm. Bake it in the ashes for a few hours and then, while it is still hot, drive in the iron blade. Then peel off the bark and with a sharp knife cut the wood into the form of a handle. Afterward, sharpen the blade with a file."

Other cooking equipment included platters and bowls made of wood and great spoons made from the horns of bighorn sheep. Smaller spoons were made of wood or pronghorn horns. Stirring rods and tongs for handling the hot stone were made of almost any available wood and were discarded after use. Jugs made from gourds of various sizes, with wooden stoppers, were used to carry water for daily use and to fill the larger water-storage jars.

Flat stones on which meat was fried were heated in the fire and then pulled to one side for use, Large, thin stones for

Gourd jugs were used to carry water to the larger storage vessels. Photo from A. F. Whiting's files, 1941.

cooking wafer (*piki*) bread were more carefully selected, but were discarded after use, unlike the Hopi practice.

Within the last century the Havasupai have obtained many metal implements and cooking utensils which are unbreakable. Although most of their old utensils had been abandoned by 1941, many of the old names or slight modifications of them were still used for their modern replacements (see Table 4.1).

COOKING METHODS

Frying

Frying (*seliika*) was not a popular method of cooking in pre-Spanish times. Even in 1941, when frying pans were available, the Havasupai preferred other techniques. The ancient method was to heat a flat rock in the fire and, when it was thoroughly heated, to pull it to one side and dust off the ashes. Meat of bighorn sheep and probably other large animals could then be fried on this hot surface.

Baking

Baking (*pava*) has long been an important method for preparing many kinds of food. The Havasupai never used fixed ovens above ground, and the Spanish type of beehive oven, which has become ubiquitous among the Pueblo Indians, was not adopted. Dutch ovens and iron stoves were rarely used, even as late as 1941. The Havasupai have, however, long been experts in the use of the earth oven (cf. Walapai *pavuk*, earth oven). A great many foods were, and still are (in 1941), cooked in a pre-heated pit in the earth. The size of the pit and complexity of the process varied, depending on what was being cooked. The basic problem of this technique was to get enough heat into the ground to cook the material completely without reducing the exterior portions of the food to charcoal.

The pit was dug in sand or earth, since gravel allowed too much heat and steam to escape. Larger pits were lined with stones which were heated by the same fire that warmed the pit. Hot stones were placed within the abdominal cavity of most of the larger animals that were cooked in such pits. Except for the very large mescal pits, a fire was built on top or to the side of the covered pit. The fire was usually allowed to die down once the ground had been thoroughly heated.

The materials to be cooked often had a natural outer layer which would be discarded before eating. Such foods needed little or no protection from dirt or ashes. Only the animals with valuable pelts were skinned, though feathers were usually plucked from birds and the quills and fur of porcupines and other creatures were singed off. Corn was not husked until after baking, and breads and tamales were either wrapped in corn husks or protected by layers of damp grass. In the larger pits pinyon twigs were specifically required, because they give flavor, as well as protection, to several meats (porcupine, bobcat, badger, and probably others).

Small birds (doves and quail) were placed in a pit dug in wet sand to protect them from cooking too quickly. With larger animals, such as porcupine, rock squirrel, woodrat, bobcat, and badger, the food itself was covered with moist sand. Even so, the topmost covering soon became dry, and a large fire or one that was maintained too long rapidly burned the contents of the pit.

Cooking time varied with the size of the item to be cooked. Squash and most of the larger game animals were usually left in the pit overnight. The food in the huge mescal pit was left considerably longer, while small game and vegetables were removed in less time. Some foods, such as mutton grass, had to be removed promptly to avoid burning.

Apparently only one kind of food was baked at any one time. Ordinarily each family cooked separately but, when groups of people hunted or collected together, they combined their respective portions in one pit. Communal baking was especially true for the preparation of mescal and appears to have also occurred for mutton grass, quail, doves, bobcats, and rabbits.

Most of the meat was baked by the men who brought it into camp. Corn and vegetables were cooked by the women. Quail, doves, and other small game were hunted, baked, and eaten by boys without taking them home.

Parching

In 1941 parching (*silcika*) was still done in a shallow basketry tray which had been lined with some protective coating. The grains and hot coals were tumbled about in the tray "by a swinging, sinuous, rotary movement." Then the lighter charcoal was separated from the grains with the same motion, by throwing it up from the far edge of the tray and blowing it away. Any larger pieces of charcoal that remained were picked out (Spier 1928). Very small grains had to be treated more quickly than large grains. Parching not only cooked the seed but also changed the flinty structure of the grain to a chalk-like consistency which was much easier to grind. Parching may partly explain the need for only a single grinding stone in contrast to the three graded stones used by the Hopi. Mutton grass and Indian millet were not parched in this manner because they had already been subjected to heat during the process of collecting.

Boiling

In addition to the pottery and basketry containers already described, a big barrel cactus was used in some temporary camps for boiling (*ta ' olka*). The spines were burned off and the top (or, if the cactus was removed from its foundations, one of the sides) was bashed in and the pulpy interior mashed and pounded until the water stored within the cactus was separated from the soft inner tissues. Stones, heated red hot in a fire, were dropped into the water with bent twig tongs. Cold stones were either removed as the cooking went on or were left until afterwards, whichever suited the convenience of the cook. Foods boiled in a barrel cactus took on a special flavor. If the people stayed in the area for some time, the cactus boiling pot was used repeatedly, until eventually the flesh became withered and useless.

Boiling was usually done by the women. Most game animals, even small ones, were cut up and dressed before cooking; this was not true when animals were baked. There is some indication that, at least for rabbits, boiling was the preferred method of cooking. Meat was boiled in salt water. Quail and hen eggs were also boiled.

Boiling for purposes other than cooking included methods for dying buckskin and for making mescal paints, arrow poisons, and medicinal teas.

HAVASUPAI RECIPES

The Havasupai used many species of plants to prepare a variety of dishes, including breads, corn dishes, dumplings, drinks, fruits, meal, seed butter, and soups (Table 4.2).

Baked Breads

Baked breads (*miyal*) were made from a variety of wild seed, as well as from corn. The grain was not parched but rather was coarsely ground on the grinding stones. A little warm water and a pinch or two of salt were added, and the dough was made into a single flat cake. A fire was built in a pit and, after the fire had burned down, the cakes—usually protected with corn husks or moistened green grass—were laid on the coals and covered with leaves. The whole thing was then covered with damp (but not wet) sand, earth, or ashes, and a fire was built on top. Estimates of cooking time vary from fifteen minutes to one hour, depending in part, no doubt, upon the materials, the amount to be cooked, and the cook herself.

Acacia Bread (*qicas-miyal*)

This bread was made from seeds of catclaw (*Acacia greggii*), which are unusually large and hard. They were parched before grinding. Otherwise, this bread was prepared as described above.

Baked Corn Bread (*tiyac-miyal* or *tiyac-miyal-pava*)

Prepared in the same way as the preceding, except that dried or green corn was used. In 1941, a little wheat flour, salt, and baking powder was added to the dry corn flour. The bread was cooked either as a single loaf or as individual portions wrapped in corn husks.

Salt-Rising Bread

In 1941 bread was frequently made of wheat flour, or a mixture of wheat and corn meal, plus water, salt, and baking powder. It was cooked over a wire grate laid on the coals, and was often prepared three times a day.

Sunflower Cakes

Sunflower (*Helianthus* spp.) seeds are quite oily. The seeds were ground, made into small cakes, and baked for a short time.

TABLE 4.2
Plants Prepared as Food

Scientific Name	Common Name
Breads	
Acacia greggii	catclaw
Chenopodium fremontii	goosefoot
Helianthus spp.	sunflowers
Koeleria cristata	June grass
Lepidium lasiocarpum	peppergrass
*Zea mays	corn
Corn Dishes	
*Zea mays	corn
Dumplings	
Amaranthus hybridus	amaranth
Chenopodium spp.	goosefoot
Oryzopsis hymenoides	Indian millet
Poa fendleriana	mutton grass
*Zea mays	corn
Drinks	
Agave utahensis	mescal
Aloysia wrightii	Wright lippa
Descurainia spp.	tansy mustards
Ephedra viridis	Mormon tea
*Ficus carica	fig
Juniperus osteosperma	juniper
Lycium pallidum	desert thorn
Opuntia phaeacantha	prickly pear
Prosopis juliflora	mesquite
*Prunus persica	peach
Rhus trilobata	squaw bush
Yucca baccata	broad-leaf yucca
Fruit	
*Citrullus vulgaris	watermelon
Boiled Greens	
Amaranthus hybridus	amaranth
Eriogonum inflatum	desert trumpet
Rumex crispus	wild rhubarb
Stanleya pinnata	desert plume

*Introduced or domesticated species

66

TABLE 4.2
(continued)

Scientific Name	Common Name
Parched or Ground Meal	
Chenopodium spp.	goosefoot, pigweeds
Helianthus spp.	sunflowers (wild & domestic)
Lepidium lasiocarpum	peppergrass
Oryzopsis hymenoides	Indian millet
Poa fendleriana	muttongrass
Zea mays	corn
Seed Butter	
Artemisia spp.	wormwoods
Descurainia spp.	tansy mustards
Gaillardia pinnatifida	blanket flower
Gilia sinuata	gilia
Helianthus spp.	sunflowers (wild & domestic)
Lepidium lasiocarpum	peppergrass
Mentzelia albicaulis	blazing star
Pinus edulis	pinyon
Soups	
Amaranthus hybridus	amaranth
Cucurbita moschata	squash
Pectis papposa	chinchweed
Phaseolus spp.	beans
Quercus gambelii	oak (acorn)
Zea mays	corn

*Introduced or domesticated species

These were eaten as a relish or as a meat substitute, particularly in summer (Cushing 1882).

Corn Dishes

Corn on the cob, raw (*tiyace*)

Corn could be eaten directly off the cob with the teeth, but the more common method was to break off kernels with the thumbnail, and place them into the palm of the same hand. When a handful was thus secured it was poured into the mouth off the side of the hand (Spier 1928).

Corn on the cob, baked (*tiyac-pa'va*)

Ears of green corn with the husks on were placed in a trench or pit in which a fire had been allowed to burn down. They were covered with earth (not sand) and a fire was built on top. When the corn was cooked, the charred husks were stripped back, the ends of the cob trimmed clean, and the ears tied in pairs by the husks to be hung up until some casual visitor came by (Spier 1928). Corn prepared in this way was frequently eaten between meals.

Pit-baking was a method of preserving sweet-tasting corn for winter storage. Unlike the Hopi usage, it was not restricted to sweet corn, but was also used for flour corn in its "milk," or "sweet," stage. Corn intended for winter storage was cooked a shorter time than that intended for immediate consumption, as it would be recooked when it was served. The baked corn was stored in rock granaries with other corn.

Corn on the cob, boiled (*tiyac-ta'ola*)

Husked green corn was sometimes boiled, but this was not a frequent method of preparation.

Corn on the cob, roasted (*tiyac-silva*)

Green corn with the husks on were roasted on a bed of hot coals. This was a common method of preparation in 1941, particularly for individuals in the fields or anyone wanting a light lunch.

Piki, or wafer, bread (*tes-viyat* or *pika*)

This dish was borrowed from the Hopi. It was made from blue corn or, if that was not available, from white corn. Unlike other Havasupai corn foods, color varieties were never mixed for this dish. The parched grains were ground fine and mixed with salted water to form a thin gruel. This was cooked on a large, thin, flat rock which was greased with pumpkin seed oil or, if it was not available, with suet. The carefully selected flat rock was temporarily propped up on smaller stones over an open fire, like a griddle.

Handfuls of the prepared liquid were spread rapidly over the rock until the surface was nearly covered. The gruel cooked quickly and started to curl at the edges. It was then grasped at two corners and peeled off the stone. While still hot and pliable, it was folded and rolled into a convenient size. The Havasupai considered it a special dish, in contrast to the Hopi, who prepared it frequently.

The Hopi origin of the dish is well known, but the date of borrowing by the Havasupai cannot be fixed. E. U., who was about forty years old in 1941, remembered stealing freshly cooked sticks of *piki* from his great-grandmother. Mrs. B. J. said the cooking method was learned while Hopi from Oraibi were resident among the Havasupai during a period of drought. The Havasupai product resembled the Hopi one, but the more colorful Hopi variations were not duplicated. These were known and admired, but E. U. insisted that Hopi piki contained more grit from the grinding stones and sometimes tasted of lard. Apparently the Havasupai did not add ashes to keep the gruel alkaline as the Hopi did. The Havasupai did not build special closets in which to keep their piki, as the Hopi did. This inattention to special storage was consistent with their general, unsettled way of life.

The written forms of the Hopi and Havasupai names for this bread are the same: *piki*. Havasupai pronunciation, however, tends to voice the consonants, so that the sound of the Havasupai word is more like *biga*. The term was known to the Havasupai but it was not in general use in 1941.

Sweetener (*Havasupai term unknown*)

Chewing corn flour in the mouth and spitting it out into a bowl where the saliva changes the starch to sugar is an old Hopi custom. Cushing (1882) reported seeing the Havasupai also use this custom.

Tamales (*tivac-kicitakova-ta'ole*)

Unparched dry corn was finely ground on a grinding stone and added to boiling salted water. It was then stirred (until it thickened) and kneaded. Individual portions were rolled in corn husks, the ends of which were then folded and tied in two places. These were then boiled twenty to thirty minutes. The Havasupai name means "corn-tied-boiled."

Drinks

Fruit and Similar Drinks

Prior to 1900, drinks were made by soaking fresh or dried foods in water. Most of the drinks were sweet or were sweetened by adding a product such as mescal. In 1941 this process had been shortened by boiling the dried food products.

In the summer the ground seeds of the tansy mustard were added to water to make a refreshing drink called *winaka*.

Teas

Two semi-medicinal teas were sometimes used as drinks. *Lippa* twigs were put into boiling water for one minute to make a tea. This was preferred to the drink made from Mormon tea. The twigs of the latter were put into cold water and brought to a boil. Boiling longer than the two minutes made this brew bitter. By 1941 the Havasupai had become confirmed coffee drinkers, although these two traditional teas were still used if coffee was temporarily unavailable.

Dumplings

Dumplings(*setuva*)

The preparation of dumplings was one of the most important methods of cooking practiced by the Havasupai. Grain, parched and ground fine on a grinding stone, was poured into boiling, salted water and stirred until it thickened. This thick paste was removed from the cooking vessel with a dipper made of bighorn sheep horn and molded into large, somewhat flattened balls about three inches in diameter. These were placed in a basket tray or plate and served.

Marbles (*ci-kata'uuika*)

Unparched grain was ground on a grinding stone and kneaded into a thick paste with a little hot, salted water. The dough was rolled between the palms into cylinders and bits were pinched off these cylinders and rolled into little balls about an inch and a half to two inches in diameter. The little bits of dough were dropped into (unsalted) boiling water and stirred occasionally. The marbles were made in considerable quantity and appear to have been a special dish.

Marbles were usually made of corn; blue corn was preferred, but other types were used if blue corn was not available. Marbles could also be made with green corn, rather than parched corn. Sometimes squash flowers were ground and cooked with the bits of dough; this process made the balls turn yellow. Marbles could also be made from mutton grass and goosefoot (*Chenopodium* spp.).

Fruits

Many fruits, both fresh and dried, were eaten plain or made into drinks (see above).

Watermelon (*suumaca*)

Watermelon, introduced within the historic period, was called *suumaca*, "to eat green, unripe," in contrast to the native pumpkin or squash, which had to be cooked before eating. It was not unusual to find a Havasupai eating watermelon by cutting open one side and cutting down into the flesh, leaving the remaining melon to form a dish for its own juice. This method is similar to the hollowing out of a barrel cactus for stone boiling.

A somewhat similar pattern also occurred with squash. Sometimes a squash was baked and carefully opened. The flesh was eaten, but care was taken to keep the shell intact.

After it was cleaned and dried, the shell was used as a storage container for such things as seeds. The walls of such a container were much thinner than those of the smaller gourd vessels, and the two types can be distinguished readily in archaeological material.

Greens

Boiled Spring Greens (*Havasupai term unknown*)

In the spring or early summer, before the flowers appeared, the young, fresh, tender leaves of several herbs were collected and cooked as greens. As a rule they were boiled "until tender," drained, balled into individual portions and served. Some cooks put salt into the water in which the greens were cooked; others added salt to the finished product.

Meal

Parched Meal (*kwetava*)

Corn was often mixed and ground with other seeds (see Table 4.2). Such mixtures could be eaten as a ground meal. A small amount pinched between thumb and fingers was put into the mouth and chewed. *Kwetwa* dried out the mouth very quickly, and liquid of some kind was an essential accompaniment. A sweet drink prepared from baked mescal was a favorite. There was considerable variation in individual ideas about which seeds could be combined or even used. Corn, as well as many of the others, could be eaten separately.

Ground Meal (*cimaq*)

Some seeds, which were heated during the collecting process, were eaten dry as ground meal (*cimaq*) in the same manner as parched meal.

Seed Butter

Seed Butter (*tahaik*)

A number of seeds with high oil content (see Table 4.2) were made into a preparation which the Havasupai likened to peanut butter. The seeds were parched and ground and, if necessary, moistened with a little water. The resulting dough was kneaded into a paste, which was eaten with drinks made from a variety of wild and domestic fruits. In 1941 seed butter was spread on bread. Seed butter was the characteristic method of preparing oily seeds. The shells of pinyon nuts and wild sunflower were not removed during the process, although those of the cultivated sunflower were.

Soups

The most common method of cooking both wild and cultivated seeds was to make a soup or mush (*sumkwin*). Often several types of seeds were combined in the process and cooked together. The resulting dish apparently varied in consistency from an almost clear liquid to a thick, oatmeal-like mush, depending to some extent upon the type of the seeds used. The seeds were parched and then ground on a grinding stone. Salted water was heated to the temperature at which a little flour sprinkled on the surface would not sink. If the test flour floated, the rest was poured in and stirred at frequent intervals with a stick. When the soup was ready, the originally white flour would be slightly yellow. Soup was formerly prepared in a coiled basket by the stone-boiling method.

Bits of meat, sometimes "parched" in the manner of the seeds, were often included in soups. Seeds with a high oil content were not parched, but ground and added directly to the hot water. They appear to have served as meat substitutes and were always added to a soup with starchy grain. The seeds of blazing star and Indian millet were often combined, since neither needed parching (the first was oily and the second was heated at the time of collecting). Beans for soup were ground without parching and were often mixed with corn. Pinyon nuts were ground up without being removed from the shells. Dry corn soup was prescribed as the only food for a new mother because it insured a free flow of milk (Spier 1928).

Green Corn Soup (*Havasupai term unknown*)

This soup was prepared during the growing season, when green corn and vegetables were available. Green corn which had been cut from the cob and ground (not pounded) on the grinding stone was added slowly to hot water. The cook would stir the mixture throughout the process. The soup was brought to a boil and removed from the fire.

Green Squash Soup (*hmte'e'vahawa-sumkwin*)

Diced young green squash might be added to the corn soup recipe above. The resulting mixture was particularly thick.

Meat Soups and Their Flavorings

Acorns were ground and added for flavor to beef or deer soups a few minutes before they had finished cooking. Acorns were not abundant and alone were not a major food resource.

Jerked meat was pounded between stones and then placed in warm water. This water might be thickened with bean flour to make a thick soup or stew (Spier 1928).

The use of the wild marigold as a condiment seems to have been learned from the Hopi.

Squash Flower (Blossom) Soup (*tetasfs-sumkwin*)

Squash flowers and/or young amaranth leaves were boiled separately and, if necessary, ground on a grinding stone. Fresh or dry corn was ground and mixed with cold water. Flowers, leaves, and corn were all then placed in the water in which the vegetables had been cooked and the soup was allowed to come to a boil.

5. Keeping Warm

Keeping warm in an environment that is often very cold is a matter of primary importance. The Havasupai kept themselves warm with fires, by constructing houses and other shelters, and by using blankets, sleeping mats, and clothing.

FIRE MAKING AND FIREWOOD

The simplest way to keep warm was to build a fire (Table 5.1 shows some fire-making terminology). The Havasupai used a number of plant and animals in their fire-making materials (Table 5.2), and started fires by either the fire-drill or the strike-a-light method. In the fire-drill method friction was caused by twisting one piece of wood in a hole in another piece of wood. The heat from the friction eventually ignited some tinder, causing a fire. Spier in 1928 wrote an excellent description of the Havasupai fire-drill method.

The strike-a-light was used in the same manner as a flint and steel were used in colonial time. Equipment—cotton tinder in a hollow tube, and pieces of chert and flint—was kept in a special container of deer or pronghorn skin. The materials were difficult to obtain, and the cotton was raised especially for this purpose from seed acquired from the Hopi. The cotton seeds were removed and the fibers spread out on a blanket. By working the cotton back and forth over the surface of the blanket,

TABLE 5.1
Fire-making Terminology

English	Havasupai
Fire	*'o'oho*
Fire drill	*'o'kaka*
Hearth of fire drill	*hatuyavuk*
Stick of the fire drill	*kaiya*
Strike-a-light	*'o'takiske*
Cotton	*hecawa*
Braided cotton wick	*hecawa-sinava*
Wildcat thigh bone	*nymiciyaake* or *nymimathile*
Flint knife	*akwa'a*
Chert	*awiqlisa'a*
"Slow match," firebrand	*'o'ho'kwiitia'*

they were gathered into roves, which were not spun, but twisted into loose threads with the fingers. The threads were then braided into a thick cord about a foot long which was, in turn, threaded into a hollow tube. The tube was usually made from the femur of a bobcat; descriptions are vague, but there is some indication that a reed might also have been used.

Flints were usually at hand, at least in the form of knives. The exact nature of the second rock has not been determined, but it was probably chert. In the strike-a-light method, the charred end of the cotton wick was pulled out of its protective tube and held, together with the chert, in one hand, and a spark was struck with the flint held in the other hand. When a spark caught in the cotton tinder it was blown to a flame, which was then used to light additional tinder. Afterwards the wick was pulled back into its protective tube, which extinguished the flame.

Once a fire was built, it was often kept burning. Where plenty of firewood was available it was a simple matter to leave large logs on the fire when leaving camp. When firewood was limited, or, when it was necessary to move camp, a "slow match," or firebrand, was employed. This consisted of a spiral coil of juniper bark tied with yucca. The ends were set on fire and kept smouldering by blowing on them at intervals. Fire

TABLE 5.2
Animals and Plants Used in Fire-making Equipment

Scientific Name	Common Name
Animals	
Antilocapra americana	pronghorn
Lynx rufus	bobcat (wildcat)
Odocoileus heminous	deer
Plants	
Amelanchier utahensis	serviceberry
Cowania mexicana	cliff-rose
Fendlera rupicola	saxifrage
Gossypium spp.	cotton
Juniperus osteosperma	juniper
Nolina microcarpa	beargrass
Phragmites communis	reed
Prosopis juliflora	mesquite
Yucca baccata	yucca

*Domesticated species

could be carried in this fashion from early dawn until noon. The Colorado was called "The River of the Firebrands" by early Spaniards who found the Yuma using similar firebrands to keep warm.

Table 5.3 shows trees used by the Havasupai for firewood. Firewood was no problem on the Plateau, where there was usually an abundance of pinyon and juniper. Winter camps were often located in relatively thick stands of juniper, which provided adequate wood supplies as well as protection from the winds. However, within the valley the only firewood available by 1941 was cottonwood, a notoriously poor fuel. Occasional trees of mesquite, ash, and similar woods were used, but they were not available in any quantity. Since by this time permanent residence within the valley was the rule, fuel was a major problem. Even though the winters are not as cold here as they are on the Plateau, the sun is far to the south and much of the village is in shadow for a large portion of the chill winter days. It is not surprising that the valley was not a winter refuge in aboriginal times.

TABLE 5.3
Plants Used for Firewood

Scientific Name	Common Name
Firewood on the Plateau	
Artemisia tridentata	sagebrush
Juniperus utahensis	juniper
Pinus edulis	pinyon
Pinus ponderosa	yellow pine
Firewood in the Valley	
Baccharis emoryi	groundsel tree
Celtis reticulata	hackberry
Fraxinus pennsylvanica	ash
Populus fremontii	cottonwood
Prosopis juliflora	mesquite
Ptelea pallida	hop tree
Salix bonplandiana	willow

HOUSES AND SHELTERS

During much of the year some form of shelter was, if not absolutely necessary, at least desirable. In the heat of summer inhabitants of this area needed shade, and in the cold of winter they needed an enclosed space which would retain the heat. The Havasupai met these needs in a variety of ways, depending upon the location and their own inclinations. Table 5.4 shows plants used in the construction of various kinds of shelter.

Under the conditions which prevailed around the middle of the nineteenth century, they built substantial houses only on the Plateau. Though occupied for only a few months in the winter, these structures were, nevertheless, relatively permanent. The basic framework of these conical huts consisted of two heavy forked poles with the butt ends firmly set into the ground on opposite sides of a circle and the forks interlocked over the center. Two additional poles were being anchored at the midpoints of the semicircles established by the first two. Between two of these posts space was left for the doorway; elsewhere more poles were laid to form a blunt, conical shelter.

TABLE 5.4
Plants Used in Shelter Construction

Scientific Name	Common Name	Location
House Poles		
Juniperus osteosperma	juniper	plateau
Pinus edulis	pinyon	plateau
Fraxinus pennsylvanica (rare)	ash	valley
Populus fremontii	cottonwood	valley
Thatch		
Apocynum medium	dogbane	plateau
Artemisia tridentata	sagebrush	plateau
Juniperus osteosperma	juniper bark	plateau
Apocynum medium	dogbane	canyon
Baccharis emoryi	groundsel tree	canyon
Nolina microcarpa	beargrass	canyon
Tessaria sericea (preferred material)	arrowweed	canyon
Populus fremontii	cottonwood	canyon
Typha domingensis	cattail	canyon

Usually the opening faced toward the southeast—the winter sunrise—and was closed by a blanket hung from a rough lintel. The better houses had two vertical doorposts. The spaces between the door frame and the conical walls of the hut were filled in, leaving a small space near the top of the cone to serve as a smoke hole. In 1941 this often provided an exit for a stove pipe. Horizontal rods were lashed around the outside of the framework, and the entire structure was then covered with brush thatch, the exact nature of which depended largely upon what was locally available. The entire structure was then covered with dirt. This type of house is common among peoples in this area, especially among the Walapai, and throughout the Great Basin. Navajo houses could often be seen in the Grand Canyon area in 1941 made in a similar way.

With permanent residence in the valley enforced upon many families by school schedules and the lack of opportunity to camp over much of their former range, this winter-type house

Traditional Havasupai wickiups, constructed of locally available materials. Photo by Robert C. Euler, 1977.

was, by 1941, being built in the valley. Here it was sometimes combined with a permanently constructed, often semi-enclosed, flat-roofed shelter. The shelter was usually separated from the conical lodge, but was often an integral part of it, forming a porch or anteroom to the conical house. The doorways of these more permanent houses were better built than formerly and were often closed with solid wood doors hung on hinges and locked with commercial padlocks.

Early photographs show that before the Havasupai took up permanent residence in the valley, the summer shelter used there was a light, low, almost hemispherical framework of bowed sapling supported by horizontal rods lashed to the frame (Hall 1907). Such shelters represented no great investment in time or materials and were quite adequate for the temporary camps during the warm summer months. Temporary camps, both within the valley and on the Plateau, were often made in the shelter of overhanging ledges. Occasionally, when more permanent camps were made, rock walls might be erected to enclose—at least partially—these natural shelters. Old walls of prehistoric ruins were also often used.

The Havasupai have experimented with other types of houses. A semi-subterranean house, which consisted of a ridge pole supported on two end poles, was quite popular in 1941. The roof sloped to the ground except at the ends, which were nearly vertical. This type of structure was used for storage and, sometimes, as living quarters. It seems to have been borrowed from the Mohave, for whom it was characteristic (Spier 1928).

Spier (1928) observed a polygonal type of house built in imitation of a Navajo hogan. This style of house was not observed in 1941. The Havasupai have long been familiar with stone construction, and in 1941, many of the agency buildings were built of stone. The Havasupai were familiar with Hopi construction methods, as can be seen in their beehive-shaped stone storage bins inside caves in the neighboring cliffs. By 1941 two stone residences had been attempted by the Havasupai in the village, but neither were very successful.

Traditional Havasupai houses, showing styles acquired from a variety of sources. Although more modern construction materials and techniques were gradually introduced, in the mid-1980s many of the above types of structures were still in use, either for storage or for actual living quarters. Sketches by A. F. Whiting.

SLEEPING MATS AND CLOTHING

Sleeping mats, which gave some protection from the cold of the ground, were made from loosely twisted ropes of cliff-rose bark. The larger ones (three feet by two and a quarter feet) were woven and held together at intervals by twined strings. Smaller mats for children were made like a braided rug, with the heavy material coiling out from the center in a spiral. Like the larger ones, the coiled mats were held together with cord of twisted cliff-rose bark or by cotton cord received in trade.

The Havasupai have been following the current local style trends in clothing for so many years that it is difficult to tell what they wore before European influences began to affect them. Materials used in the preparation, dyeing, and decoration of traditional clothing are shown in Table 5.5. In all probability the men wore a breechcloth of bark or skin. Several types of skin may have been used, including deer, rabbit, or bobcat. Sandals were made of woven juniper bark. The women wore two aprons of cliff-rose bark. These aprons must have looked something like an animal's tail, for the name for a woman's dress still translates as "a tail."

In cold weather blankets or robes were added as clothing. Men preferred a lightweight blanket of deer or pronghorn hide or a fur robe made by sewing several skins of bobcat or coyote together. Bears and wolves were relatively scarce, but their skins may have been used occasionally. These robes were sometimes caught at the waist with braided belts of unspun Indian hemp. Women sometimes used a heavier blanket woven of rabbit skins. Over fifty rabbits (jackrabbits or cottontails) were needed to make a blanket. The skins were torn spirally with the fingernails (never cut with a knife) into long strips about an inch wide. Two of these strips were then twisted together on the thigh, or, according to one informant, the skin might be wrapped around a stronger strip of cliff-rose bark. Apparently the skins were torn and twisted when they were fresh, and the resulting cords then stretched outside until dry.

TABLE 5.5
Materials Used in Making Clothing

Scientific Name	Common Name
Animals	
Antilocapra americana	pronghorn
Canis latrans	coyote
Canis lupus	wolf
Cervus canadensis	elk
Equus caballus	horse
Lepus californicus	jackrabbit
Lynx rufus	bobcat
Odocoileus hemionus	deer
Sylvilagus audubonii	cottontail rabbit
Taxidea taxus	badger
Ursus americanus	bear
Plants	
Apocynum spp.	dogbane or Indian hemp
Berberis fremontii	holly grape
Cercocarpus ledifolius	mountain mahogany
Cowania mexicana	cliff-rose
Gossypium spp.	cotton
Juniperus osteosperma	juniper
Tessaria sericea	arrowweed
Yucca baccata	yucca
Mineral	
Hematite	red mineral dye

When enough cord had been assembled, weaving could begin. Only women made blankets. Small blankets might be worn, but they were mostly used as sleeping mats.

The items of clothing described above could hardly have been adequate for the sharp, cold winters, even if robes were used extensively. The people supplemented these by wrapping their legs in strips of tanned skin. We know that, at least in relatively recent times, they covered their hands with something that resembled muffs, rather than gloves. The muffs were made of coyote, elk, or possibly other furs. Overshoes for winter wear were made from buckskin or badger, as well as other furs. The neck and shoulders were protected by a bobcat skin similar to that worn by certain Hopi kachinas.

Various type of leather clothing have been described by Spier (1928). In addition to leather shirts, the men sometimes wore two-piece leather moccasins, leather leggings, and knee-length trousers with openings at the sides decorated with silver buttons. In the twentieth century the women, too, began to wear moccasins—large, heavy affairs, with a long and elaborate flap which wound around the lower leg. These were distinctly reminiscent of similar types found among Hopi women.

The tanned leather clothing of the Havasupai was often colorful. The bright yellow fibers of the roots of the holly grape was used for a yellow dye. The roots were collected in the form of chips and these were smashed up and boiled in water until a thick concoction was obtained. This was brushed into the leather and allowed to dry. Sometimes red mineral paint was boiled with it, though this was considered inferior to the red dye obtained from the inner bark of the mountain mahogany. To make red mahogany dye, the bark was removed with a knife when the wood was dry, and a pound or two was put in water and boiled for two hours. When it cooled, the liquid was brushed onto the buckskin and worked into the surface of the leather with a brush.

Leather clothing was decorated with fringes and with a variety of tinklers of metal or, earlier, of dew claws or short bone tubes. Old women's dresses were sometimes decorated with deer eyes that had been drained of their fluid, inflated, dried, and made into rattles by inserting a kernel of corn into each one before the opening was sewn up. Detailed analysis of clothing styles in this area has shown that the Havasupai adopted the tailored skin clothing which had been developed on the Plains. The Plains Indians decorated their clothing by adding an extra piece of triangular, fringed leather on the front of the item and a more-or-less exact duplicate in the rear. The tailored leather shirts adopted by the Havasupai retained one of these decorative triangular flaps, as did the skin aprons which the women began to wear in the early 1900s.

In the years that have passed, new styles came with missionaries and with contact with Euro-American stores and mail-order houses. Beginning about the turn of the century the women adopted a huge, Mother-Hubbard dress. This dress was still standard for older women in the group in 1941, but the younger women and the men followed styles offered in stores in adjacent white communities.

Tanning Animal Skins

Since much of the traditional winter clothing was made of furs and skin, tanning techniques were of considerable importance. Spier (1928) has given an extended, detailed account of the procedures involved in the preparation of skins: At the time a deer was butchered the brains and the marrow from the spinal column were collected for use in tanning, and the sinew was saved for sewing. The hide itself was carefully folded, flesh side in, to prevent drying on the way home. Back in camp the hide was stretched out, weighted down with stones, and allowed to dry for four or five days. It was then sprinkled with enough water to make it pliable and rolled into a loose cylinder for storage. Meanwhile, the fresh brains were roasted, shaped into a ball, and dried over hot coals. In this form the material could be kept indefinitely.

Within the next three or four months the skin had to be tanned. Mountain lion and deer skin were sometimes tanned with the hair on, but usually the hide had to be dehaired. The job was started at dawn after the skin had soaked in the river for at least twenty-four hours. It took about two hours to stretch the skin over a pole and scrape the hair off. Formerly a cannon bone or a hip bone of a deer, which had been split lengthwise and sharpened, was used. More recently horse ribs were used instead. After it had been scraped, the skin was allowed to dry for a day or two.

Before tanning, the skin was again soaked overnight, worked until it was pliable, and then wrung dry and stretched out. A soapy liquid obtained by soaking one of the previously prepared balls of brains in water, was sprayed from the mouth over the hair side of the skin. The hide was then rolled up until the tanning agent penetrated thoroughly. After the skin dried, it was worked, pulled, rubbed, and stretched at least twice. It might be given a final stretching and pegged out with arrowweed pegs. Throughout the process care had to be taken that the skin did not get dirty. Tanning was a long and physically difficult job which many people preferred not to bother with. In 1941 the Havasupai would often barter whatever they could in order to get other people to tan their buckskin for them.

6. What to Do in Your Spare Time

Much has been said about lack of free time in a hunting-gathering culture. To be sure, there were periods of intense labor in Havasupai society, but there was also a good deal of free time between these work periods. Various types of activities absorbed people's interests and attentions beyond the normal routines of daily life. The use of a sweat lodge and games and gambling were the most common leisure activities. Tobacco was used for pleasure, but intoxicants played a minor part. Raiding and warfare were practiced by the Havasupai, but these activities were relatively uncommon.

THE SWEAT LODGE

During most of the year the spare time of a Havasupai man was absorbed in the use of the sweat lodge. Wherever the Havasupai congregated, there was sure to be a sweat lodge. The two types of lodges used were essentially miniature editions of the aboriginal houses described in Chapter 5. On the Plateau they used a small, permanent, conical hut covered with bark and earth, the floor of which was covered with bark. The other type of lodge, typical for the valley and temporary camps, consisted of a hemispherical framework of bent saplings, which was covered with blankets when it was in use.

A sweat lodge of the type used on the Plateau. The small, conical structure was covered with bark and earth. Photo by Robert C. Euler, 1956.

As a log fire burned within the lodge, two or three scores of rocks were placed around it, so as to become thoroughly heated. At intervals water was sprinkled on the hot stones to produce steam, which raised the temperature to well over 130°F. The only clothes worn were a breech-cloth (women, who occasionally used the sweat lodge, wore only an under-skirt). Only four men could use the lodge at the same time, but since the stay within the steam-filled hut was limited, and four visits were made in the sequence of an afternoon, the men could alternate in using the lodge. After leaving the lodge the person plunged into the creek or water was poured over him, if it was available.

The sweat lodge was considered to be relaxing and, at times, specifically medicinal. Most of the songs sung within the lodge were for entertainment, but there were certain curing songs which might be sung upon special occasions. In the summer-time, the sweat lodge served as a focus of men's social activity.

DANCES AND GAMES

The Havasupai and the Walapai performed dances whenever groups of people gathered together for festive occasions. Among the Havasupai these usually occurred during the early part of the harvest season, when there was, for once, plenty to eat. The country at this time was passable, since there was water in the water holes from the late summer rains. Word went out, and at the appointed time friends and acquaintances from neighboring tribes came to join in the festivities. The evenings were given over to dancing.

At a harvest festival in the fall of 1941, early in the evening, the song leader seated himself upon a chair, grasped a drum and, assisted by several men, began to sing. After some initial reluctance a circle was formed, with men and women casually interspersed, facing the drummer and singers. This circle rotated clockwise with slow, shuffling steps that were enlivened now and then by the sound of jangling spurs on the men's boots. Units of bright color followed one another across the narrow range of the firelight, the bright blues, reds, and yellows of the young men's cowboy shirts alternating with the less colorful women's dresses. The dance was punctuated by an occasional "pillar of fire," which was a red shawl made of uncut bandana cloth, two handkerchiefs wide and three or four long, which was brought into view on the broad back of a portly, visiting Mohave woman. Men and women, including visiting Navajo, Walapai, Mohave, and whites, broke into the circle at will. A small group of Mohave, who sat facing each other on two rows of chairs, sang vigorously to their own rattle accompaniment without any apparent relation to the Havasupai drum rhythm, melody, singers, or dancers. The resulting combination of sounds did not apparently disturb either group of singers. Perhaps the Mohave singing was to be equated with the singing of attendants at shamanistic performances, "to aid the performers." Similar singing by visiting groups of Navajo and Hopi was observed by Spier (1928).

The drum was made of a hollow cottonwood log with heads of skin. The Havasupai often got such drums in trade from the Hopi, although they had learned how to make them and occasionally did make their own. This drum seems to have replaced an earlier type made by stretching a skin over the mouth of a pottery vessel in which there was a little water. A thin loop of bent wood was used as a drumstick. This type of drumstick was also used among the eastern neighbors of the Havasupai and may have been borrowed from them. The harvest-festival dances were held on four consecutive nights. In earlier times the dances were preceded in the afternoons by athletic contests. By 1941 these contests had been replaced by an all-Indian rodeo.

The festival dances of the Havasupai were considered to be vaguely beneficial, to promote the well-being of the group, and there has been some suggestion that they may even have helped to produce rain. The main motivations, however, were pleasure and such economic benefits as may have come from the trade and gambling which accompanied these periods of festivities.

In their leisure time people could tell any kind of story and play any kind of a game that suited their fancy. The basic outlook of a people was, therefore, readily apparent in the things which they chose to do in their spare time. Unlike the Hopi, the Havasupai were highly individualistic in their way of life and in their way of thinking, and this individuality was reflected in their choice of amusements. The Havasupai loved games in which skill and chance were both important. They ran races, and people bet on them. After they obtained horses, they raced and bet on horses. If they were too old to ride, they lent their good horses to others and bet even more. The fact that they were not riding made it possible to circulate among the guests and talk a little longer and a little louder about their horses. When the rodeo came along the young men put up their entry fees and rode anything that came out of the chutes. They still bet.

In quieter moments in 1941 people played various games (materials used in Havasupai games are shown in Table 6.1). One such game was hidden ball, played with a ball carved from the root of the wild gourd. The player, holding the ball in one hand, made a ridge of sand. When he had divided this ridge into four hills, the ball was buried in one of them. The opponent attempted to guess which hill hid the ball. Score was kept with counters made of sections of narrow-leaved yucca. Several men could play on a side. Betting was, of course, essential. Only what one had at hand was gambled—one did not gamble with the fundamental rights of land ownership or the right to collect next year's pinyon crop.

Basket dice was a game played in the winter by women, with four on a side. The four dice were made of split femora, with bands of red paint across the hollow of the bones. They were tossed in a basket tray, and a score was made when all four were alike. Two of a kind was a miss. There were ten or more counters, and the game usually continued until one side had won all of the counters (Spier 1928). B.B., who said nothing about the game's being played by women, gave the scoring as

TABLE 6.1
Animals and Plants Used in Games and Other Recreation

Scientific Name	Common Name
Animals	
Lepus californicus	jackrabbit
Lynx rufus	bobcat
Odocoileus hemionus	deer
Sylvilagus audubonii	cottontail rabbit
Plants	
Apocynum spp.	dogbane
Baccharis emoryi	groundsel tree
Datura metaloides	jimson weed
Echinocactus spp.	barrel cacti
Eriogonum inflatum	desert trumpet
Equistetum spp.	horsetails
Fraxinus pennsylvanica	ash
Juniperus osteosperma	juniper
Laginaria vulgaris	gourd
Nicotiana attenuata	tobacco
Opuntia spp.	prickly pears
Prunus persica	peach
Salix exigua	willow
Sarcostemma cynanchoides	climbing milkweed
Scirpus spp.	rushes
Typha domingensis	cattail
Vitis arizonica	grape
Yucca angustissima	narrow-leaved yucca
Yucca baccata	broad-leaved yucca
*Zea mays	corn

*Domesticated species

follows: "All with flat or slit side up, score 5; all with round side up, score 10; two red and two round, play passes to opposite side; all other combinations, continue to play. When a score of 60 is reached, the game is won."

Several different target games were played by boys and men. Men shot at cactus targets, at wads of bark, or at flat, circular, prickly-pear joints from which the spines had been burned and scraped off, so that they could be rolled back and forth across

Nineteenth-century Havasupai girls playing a typical stick game. Photo by George Wharton James, ca. 1898, courtesy Southwest Museum.

the target area. Small barrel cacti, similarly treated, were rolled down a hill and called a bighorn sheep or some other game animal. This game still survived in 1941 except that children used a toy lariat instead of the bow and arrow. For small children simple bows were made with toy arrows of cattail. Boys often threw toy spears made of a corncob mounted on a stick at a rolling basket tray.

Another target game played by boys used a bundle of willow bark for a target. The target was thrown a distance of ten or twenty feet and everyone shot at it. If more than one person hit the target, everyone shot again. Those who missed gave the winner one arrow. To keep the arrow, however, the winner had to take the target in his left hand, toss it into the air, and hit it again. If the winner failed to vindicate his superiority in this second trial, the arrow was returned.

A cup and pin game, made of a cottontail or jackrabbit skull tied with a piece of string to a sharp stick, was played by the men. The base of the skull was cut away and the teeth removed. The skull, attached by a short cord, was tossed into the air and caught on the stick. Scoring was based upon the particular hole in the skull in which the stick was lodged.

There were a number of other adult and children's games played by the Havasupai. Most of these games were described by Spier in 1928.

TOBACCO

There was no evidence that the Havasupai ever used tobacco ceremonially, although they were aware of the Hopi ritual usages. Smoking seems to have been a pleasure. In ancient times people sometimes planted the wild seeds, often in burned areas, to ensure a crop. The preferred tobacco was *Nicotiana attenuata*; *Nicotiana trigonophylla* ("Coyote Tobacco") was little used.

Before wild tobacco could be collected, a speech had to be made to the plant. Then the leaves and possibly the seed pods (but not the flowers) were removed, dried in the sun, and ground up in the hands. Since the tobacco was very strong, it was mixed with deer grease to provide a cooler smoke. The mixture was stirred constantly in a pan which was held over a low fire for about half an hour. The tobacco was then stored in a sack made from the skin of a rock squirrel (D.I.).

Pipes were made of clay. An old style was conical in shape, with a hole in the base. The smoker had to tip his head back and hold the pipe nearly vertical, so ashes sometimes fell into his eye (E.U., quoting an older Havasupai man). In 1941 the typical pipe (*imalu'u* [from *imal*, container, and *u'uuva*, tobacco]) was made of clay obtained from the creekbed (Spier 1928). The bowl, about two inches high, was fitted with an arrow-reed stem about three inches long. Corn husk cigarettes (*u'uuva-sumkwitka*) were also used.

A boy should not smoke until he had killed a coyote: "Coyotes are hard to kill. I guess they don't want you to smoke too soon (E.U.)." Only a few of the older people smoked the native tobacco in 1941, but commercial tobacco, especially cigarettes, was in demand.

INTOXICANTS

In 1941 the Havasupai did not drink much liquor, perhaps due, in part, to their isolation from any source of supply. They manufactured no intoxicating drinks of their own. The use of jimson weed (*datura meteloides*) was minor and unimportant— the fascination it held for the Havasupai was largely that of forbidden fruit. Its intoxicating properties were well known, and the older men cautioned against its use. Nevertheless, there appeared to be few men who had not tried it at one time or another, "just to see what would happen." A few leaves or a couple of seeds were said to be enough to intoxicate a person for a day or more. The throat went dry, and the victim did not know what he was doing, bumped into objects, and even hoed up his own corn (Spier 1928). The tales told of its use were enough to make any adventurous young man want to try it; the results were such that the performance was rarely repeated.

RAIDING AND WARFARE

The Havasupai had little to gain from raiding their relatively poor neighbors to the north and to the south, and there was no point in raiding the numerically superior Hopi to the east, with whom trade and friendly relationships were well established. To the west were their friends and relatives, the Walapai. Relations with the Navajo were at first hostile, especially as this tribe began to encroach upon Havasupai territory in the 1860s. The Navajo at that time were recovering from the Bosque Redondo experience and were in no mood to fight. Occasional robbings and murders by highway thieves occurred, but there were never any pitched battles between the two groups. Most of the Havasupai fights were with the Yavapai or the Paiute, and the Havasupai were not the aggressors.

Raids upon the Havasupai by other tribes were primarily for plunder, though women captives were occasionally taken. The horse represented convenient, readily marketable, and self-transporting booty. The development of horse herds, as well as stocks of agricultural produce by the Havasupai, must have been the basic incentive for their enemies to raid them. Their own raids were usually organized for purposes of retaliation. Since their numbers were small, raids were usually conducted in conjunction with the Walapai.

Populations in this area were small and anything more than minor raids would have reduced the populations of the warring bands with considerable rapidity. Raids were infrequent, probably not averaging more than one a year, and loss of life was slight. In the three Yavapai raids reported by Spier (1928) the total loss of life was only eight Yavapai and two Havasupai. Fights between the Yavapai and Walapai and between the Walapai and the Paiute, in which Havasupai participated, were much more deadly and at times resulted in the virtual annihilation of the entire raiding party (Spier 1928). The basic motivation for most Havasupai raids was not the annihilation of the enemy, but retaliation or the acquisition of goods.

Battle techniques were closely adjusted to the weapons available. In addition to items used in hunting, there were clubs, armor, and poisoned arrows. The heavy, wooden-shafted arrows designed for large game were used in warfare. The poison used on the arrows was said to cause death even if the enemy was just scratched by it. The poison was applied to the tips of the arrows, using as an adhesive either deer's blood or juice which had been wrung from the leaves of the broad-leaved yucca. The ingredients of this poison probably varied, but it is reported to have included the poison from scorpions, centipedes, red ants, spiders, jimson weed, and hop tree (Table 6.2).

The methods of attack were well known, and at times involved the organization of a number of men. The men in the front line wore heavy, double-skin robes and loosely twisted buckskin mufflers around their necks. A bundle of buckskin, with a thong handle, was held in the left hand and used as a shield to protect the head. A club with a large, round ball, or head, was carried in the right hand. Sometimes, when more than two men were advancing as a unit, the leaders carried heavy buckskin curtains suspended from a stick or bow. This skin curtain was held high enough to protect the faces of the carriers. Several such men together formed a solid front which arrows could not penetrate. At intervals, the curtain would be lowered to permit the archers to shoot at the enemy. Should one of the curtain bearers be hit, they would all retreat to a safe distance where the remaining group re-formed and then readvanced. When feasible, the members of the attacking party all shot arrows at the same time, thus making it impossible for the attacked individuals to escape a hit by dodging. When the terrain was favorable, the party being attacked was isolated and forced to expend all its arrows. A mass attack could then finish them off with ease (Spier 1928).

After 1850 the picture began to change. The Havasupai replaced the ball-headed clubs with metal hatchets obtained from the Hopi in trade (Spier 1928). Around 1855 three Yavapai raiders set out in what appears to have been their usual, light-hearted fashion for a gentlemanly raid upon the Havasupai.

TABLE 6.2
Animals and Plants Used in Arrow Poison

Scientific Name	Common Name
Animals	
Chilopoda	centipedes
Latrodectus mactans	black widow spider
Odocoileus hemionus	deer
Pogonomyrmex spp.	harvester ants
Scorpionida	scorpions
Plants	
Datura spp.	jimson weeds
Ptelea pallida	hop tree
Yucca baccata	yucca

They were met by what was, for them, a strange, new weapon which fired a metal bullet instead of an arrow. At that time the Havasupai had only three guns and a pistol (Spier 1928). By 1865, however, the Havasupai had acquired plenty of guns through trade with the Paiutes and Utes (Spier 1928), and warfare became a serious business.

Although raiding and warfare were conducted in the tribe's "spare time," it would be a mistake to assume that such activities were ever considered "recreation." There was danger, even without iron hatchets and guns. A couple of wild-eyed young men could arouse the wrath of a neighboring group and expose the entire village to the danger of retaliatory raids. For this reason, raiding parties tended to be organized, and the permission—if not the participation—of a chief was usually essential.

Scalping was not an old pattern among the Havasupai. It seems to have been learned in relatively late times. After 1800, the Havasupai did take the scalps of slain Yavapai. These were hung on a pole in the center of a clearing. The warriors, joined by the other men and women of the group, formed a circle and danced a sidewise step around the trophies, yelling, calling, and breaking the voice by placing the hand over the mouth at regular intervals.

7. The Need for a Mate

Although Havasupai culture was definitely oriented around the men and their activities, women played an important part and were essential to the basic functioning of the group. Duties were sharply divided, and the women's share, if not overly glamorous, was nonetheless essential. In general, women collected the plant products and men hunted. The cooking was entrusted to the women, except for pit-baking, which often involved a great deal of labor. An adult woman was necessary for the proper economic functioning of any household. Only in rare cases did the men take over the female tasks and maintain a bachelor household.

The number of active adult women limited the number of functioning household units, especially if there were fewer women than men, as was true in 1941. Spier (1922a) had noted something very similar in about 1920. One would expect that this emphasis upon the importance of women might have tended to increase their status in the society. If these relatively large household groups, centering around adult women, had persisted as social units, they might well have taken on special significance and eventually might even have produced the type of social structure we call clans, as found among the Hopi. However, there was no tendency among the Havasupai for these groups to persist. The central role in these households was not passed on from mother to daughter or from mother to daughter-in-law. In the absence of an adult woman the members of the household dispersed. Often there was no possibility of replacing such a central figure. Women of her age were scarce, and even if a younger man, such as the older son, was married, his wife may have been reluctant to take on the responsibility for such a large household unit. More often than not the young couple established themselves as an independent household. So upon the death of the older woman, those who were left tended to drift off to other family groups. In such cases the older men who continued to occupy the house would eat with some younger relatives in the vicinity.

ATTRACTING THE OPPOSITE SEX

When a young man wanted to settle down and get married, he would look for a girl. If he had land within the Havasupai colony, or had reasonably good prospects of inheriting some, he would remain within the community; otherwise, he was likely to find work outside. His immediate problem was to make himself acceptable to the girl in question, so he turned attention to his personal appearance. The girl did likewise. Table 7.1 lists some of the materials used in personal adornment.

The girl, in former times, started taking particular pains with her face painting. She may even have had a little tattoo, a vertical line or several lines on the chin, and maybe a line of dots together with several lines on the chin. The face painting tended to be more elaborate than tattoos. Red paint (hematite) was obtained in a mine to the west, while black paint came from a surface deposit in the Walapai country. White gypsum, found locally, was roasted shortly before using it, to form a white powder (plaster of Paris). There was a blue-gray paint of mineral origin which was less commonly used. A brown paint was prepared from the burned heads of baked mescal. Face paint was applied with a brush of yucca fibers.

TABLE 7.1
Materials Used in Personal Adornment

Scientific Name	Common Name
Animals	
Aquila chrysaetos	Golden Eagle
Buteo regalis	Ferruginous Hawk
Erethizon dorsatum	porcupine
Lynx rufus	bobcat
Ovis canadensis	bighorn sheep
Rhopalocera	butterflies
Plants	
Agave Utahensis	mescal
Dalea spp.	wild indigos
Echinocactus spp.	barrel cacti
Opuntia spp.	prickly pears
Pinus edulis	pinyon gum
Xylorhiza tortifolia	aster
Yucca spp.	yuccas
Minerals	
Calcium sulfate	gypsum
Ferric oxide	hematite

Men also occasionally used paint and were sometimes tattooed with "T"-shaped or other designs in the middle of the forehead. In 1941 a man was more likely to have a small design (usually black stripes on a red base) tattooed on the back of the hand or on the arm. The area to be tattooed was moistened with saliva and the design drawn with a sharp stick. The design was punctured into the skin using a sharp cactus needle (prickly pear), which had been rubbed in ground charcoal. An attempt was made to stick it well down into the skin. More charcoal was sometimes rubbed into the holes during the following few days, but within a week or two it had healed. The boys let the girls tattoo them.

The Havasupai wore their hair long, and not always too well anchored in place. For the youngster with unruly hair, grease from bighorn sheep was available. It also gave the hair a luster which was considered attractive (Spier 1928). The hair of the men was worn in bangs across the forehead, and the remaining hair was parted, pulled back, and tied in a knot at the nape of the neck. This was held with a woven band of Hopi or Navajo manufacture, with the hair of the porcupine, or with a buckskin strap which, in turn, might be decorated with porcupine quills (Spier 1928). The men's traditional hair style had nearly disappeared by 1941. The women's hair was cut at the level of the shoulders in the back and at the level of the eyebrows across the front. In 1941 the women still used a hair brush made from mescal fibers. The brushes were bent over in the middle, tied, and the end covered with buckskin attached with pinyon gum.

When Cushing visited the Havasupai in the early summer of 1881, he described the hair of the boys as being "closely cut, with the exception of a very small tuft at the crown, five to seven inches in length, looking not unlike the plume of a California quail, which I believe it imitates" (Cushing 1882). In 1941 various informants denied the occurrence of such a style.

Downy eagle feathers, attached to a short string, might be tied into the hair at the top of the head. Plumes, possibly attached to a comb or peg, were sometimes worn over the right temple (Spier 1928).

The Havasupai wore jewelry, but not to the extent of their more prosperous neighbors. It included beads from the Mohave and the Hopi. Cushing (1882) reported that they wore huge earrings of silver or beaded cactus thorns. Plugs of colored wood or, later, buttons were stuck into the ears, which were pierced up to four times. Necklaces were made of bobcat bones and rings of the flat thorns of the barrel cactus.

There was some use of perfumes. Some of these were worn by both men and women with the idea of counteracting body odors and the smell of unwashed buckskin clothing, but there were also perfumes specifically used by men to attract women. The flowers of the introduced clovers were always pointed out as being used for perfume, as was the desert aster (*Xylorhiza tortifolia*). An unidentified plant called *painyuiya* was also used.

COURTING AND MARRIAGE

A boy who had been watching the girls at the dances and had reason to suppose that he had some chance of success, might take the notion into his head that he wanted to get married. The following is Spier's 1928 description of what came next:

> When a young man wants to marry a good-looking girl, with whom he had talked, he went at night and waited close to her house until her relatives were sleeping; then he crept into her bed and shook her awake. If the girl did not want him she yelled, but the boy would not want her parents to see him, so he would go right out and return home. Someone would tell her relatives who the boy was. Then the parents would say to the girl, "The one who wants to marry you is a good boy; we want you to take him. He works well, he is not lazy; he is a good traveler and hunter; he has plenty of horses and other property. He is pretty good. If he comes again, do not yell; we like the boy." When the boy comes again she receives him. But if the parents do not like him, they say, "We do not like you; you cannot marry our daughter." If the girl receives him, they sleep together for four or five nights. Then the boy thinks of what he will give the parents. Long ago the boys gave horses, buckskin, meat, corn, pinyon nuts, mescal, or other things to eat to the parents. The boy then stayed at her parents' house for a year or so, until the couple wanted to establish their own house. He would gather wood, plant, and hunt for her parents, work for them. He would stay with his wife's parents until the couple had one or two children. If the girl or boy is lazy, or fights or does wrong, they returned the presents and terminated the affair.

The situation was much the same in 1941: essentially the man just moved in, bringing with him food and other presents so that he did not become a sudden burden upon his wife's household. If there were no objections, he stayed. Although there was no marriage ceremony preceding this arrangement, at the woman's first menstruation following marriage, the mothers of the couple washed the entire bodies of their respective children with yucca root suds, and, tying the hair back from their faces, painted them red from head to foot. This ceremony, which took place at the home of the bride's parents, concluded with a moral lecture, and both the boy and the girl were sent out to run. Racing and bathing continued for four days. For the first year after marriage, or until one or two children were born, the young people usually lived with the wife's parents.

8. Maintaining a Healthy Family

For the Havasupai, good health depended not only upon specific remedies, but also upon observing taboos and carrying out certain prescribed behavior for various important occasions. A specific illness could be caused by certain animals or plants (Table 8.1), or it could be caused by a spirit, in which case a medicine man might be called in to effect a cure (see the section on controlling the spirit world in Chapter 9 for a full discussion of the role of the shaman). For the most part, however, individual families were responsible for maintaining the general good health of their members and for administering routine treatment for minor physical ailments.

PREPARATIONS FOR CONCEPTION AND BIRTH

Conception usually took place soon after marriage. If it did not, there were certain remedies which might be tried. A piece of abalone shell, about a half-inch square, was broken up and ground to a fine powder. This was mixed with water and administered to the patient as a drink. In a variation of this remedy, a rodent (*koitu'u*) was skinned, dried, ground, and similarly administered. The shell seems to have been the preferred remedy.

TABLE 8.1
Animals and Plants That Can Cause Illness

Scientific Name	Common Name
Animals	
Apidae	bees and wasps
Crotalus spp.	rattlesnakes
Latrodectus mactans	black widow spider
Lonchaeidae	biting flies
Pogonomyrmex spp.	harvester ants
Scolopender	centipede
Scorpionidae	scorpions
Spilogale gracilis	little spotted skunk
Stenopelmatus fucus	Jerusalem cricket*
Plants	
Agaricales	mushrooms
Shepherdia rotundifolia	buffalo berry
Sphaeralcea spp.	sore eyes (globe-mallows)

*The bite of the Jerusalem cricket is painful, but otherwise harmless.

Once conception took place, certain precautions were necessary if the infant was to develop properly. Father and mother had to avoid certain meats which were in themselves dangerous, as well as those which might have been contaminated by a dangerous animal. If they did not do this, the baby would get sick, his eyes would sink in, and his belly would ache, followed by diarrhea. This precaution continued in force long after the child had been born (Spier 1982). If the mother used her left hand too much, the child would be lefthanded (Spier 1928). Similarly, if the parent killed a snake at this time it might cause the child to crawl on his stomach like a snake throughout his life. If a pregnant woman should hear the cry of a duck, hawk, or a mourning dove, her child might later sicken and die.

Both the father and the mother had to refrain from eating all meats from a month before the child was due until a month after the birth. The mother had to avoid salt not only before the child came, but also throughout the nursing period, for salt tends to dry things up, just as salt on the ground makes it hard (Spier 1928). Intercourse was also avoided during pregnancy, and the mother was not supposed to scratch her body with her fingers, although she might safely use a stick to scratch herself. There was some guessing as to the sex of the unborn infant; string figures were constructed in order to see if they would resemble a boy or a girl.

When the girl's time was near, she usually went home to her mother if she was not there already. She was carefully watched and rarely stayed alone. Her mother or another female relative assisted at the birth. If the baby was slow in coming, pressure might be applied both to the front and sides of the abdomen. The father, husband, or brother might be called in to help at this point. At delivery, the woman was seated before a hole which had been dug to receive the child. A blanket was nested in the hole. As soon as the baby arrived, the umbilical cord was squeezed and tied tightly an inch from the body and then cut. Pressure was applied to the mother's abdomen to cause the ejection of the placenta. This was buried deeply so that animals could not eat it; should they do so, the woman would become barren. The woman then stood erect to have a broad, woven, Hopi belt bound tightly around her abdomen in order to force out the fluids. Should this practice be neglected, it was feared the fluids would flow into the top of the womb, causing death.

Following the birth, mother, child, and father were bathed in yucca suds. The mother would then lie down on a heated bed made by burying hot stones under moist sand. When the stones grew cold they were replaced by hot ones. At this time herbs were not used for either an external poultice or for a medicinal tea, but the mother might drink some soup made from dry corn. These practices were continued for the next three nights.

INFANT CARE

The baby was given the breast two days after birth. If the baby was a boy, the father would run early each morning during at least the first month, a mile north and then back, in order that

TABLE 8.2
Plants Used to Make a Cradleboard

Scientific Name	Common Name
Acacia greggii	catclaw
Amelanchier utahensis	serviceberry
Cowania mexicana	cliff-rose
Fallugia paradoxa	Apache plume
Fraxinus pennsylvanica	ash
Pinus edulis	pinyon
Prosopis juliflora	mesquite
Quercus gambelii	Gambel oak
Quercus turbinella	scrub oak
Rhus trilobata	squaw bush
Tessaria sericea	arrowweed

the boy might grow up to chase the deer. The child, the mother, and the father were bathed in yucca suds every four days for the first month. If the child was chapped, powdered red paint might be sprinkled over him. When the baby was one day old, the lobes of his ears were pierced with a sharp twig by a relative or friend of the family. A cotton cord was looped through the hole to keep it open, and deer or bighorn sheep grease was smeared on to soothe the pain (Spier 1928). Care was exercised to make sure that the child was not bitten by a Jerusalem cricket which, it was thought, might suck its blood. Actually, this creature is only capable of giving a sharp but harmless bite.

The care of the infant was aided by the use of a cradleboard, which was prepared by the baby's maternal grandmother or great-grandmother before the child was born. Table 8.2 shows the plants used to construct a cradleboard. First the woman made an oval frame of hardwood, such as ash, serviceberry, scrub oak, gambel oak, or mesquite. A branch was bent into an oval while it was still green and lashed into shape. Larger frames had parallel sides with semicircular ends and might be made of two U-shaped pieces lashed together. When the frame had dried thoroughly in damp sand, a solid row of cross pieces,

a.

b.

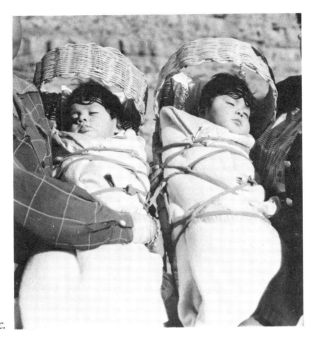

c.

*A cradleboard, made by the baby's maternal grand-
mother or great-grandmother, played an important part
in infant care: a) attaching the crosspieces to the frame;
b) the finished cradleboard; c) Havasupai twins wrapped
on cradleboards. Photos by Carma Lee Smithson, 1962,
courtesy of Robert C. Euler.*

made of arrowweed or Apache plume, was lashed onto the
underside with strips of rawhide or cotton cloth. These wrappings were smoothed over with a layer of pinyon pitch. At the
head end was a broad circular band of basket-like materials
fastened over the child's head. Because of this band, blankets
could be laid over the cradle without resting on the child's face.
Should the cradle accidentally fall, the child's face was protected by this excellent, flexible "bumper." The bumper was
made of catclaw, squawberry, or other light twigs.

Four buckskin thongs along the edge of the cradleboard formed the loops to which were attached the wrappings that secured the baby. Padding, absorbent and disposable, was made of finely pounded cliff-rose bark. The child, usually wrapped in blankets of Hopi or commercial manufacture, was kept on the cradleboard until he was ready to walk. When a child outgrew his cradleboard it might be laid aside for the next child or discarded, but it was never burned, as this would cause barrenness (Spier 1928).

The cradleboard was often decorated with beads or the dewclaws of deer hung together to form a rattle. The baby's first thin hair was sometimes clipped off and wrapped into little cloth bundles which swung from the loop above the baby's head. This was done so that the hair would grow thick. When the end of the umbilical cord dropped off, it was similarly wrapped and hung on the loop. If this was lost or thrown away, the child might grow up idiotic. When at last the child could walk, the dry cord was ground to a powder which was smeared longitudinally around the body from head to crotch and up the back to the head. This was done so that the cord should not be lost, i.e., it was returned to the child's body so that he would always have it.

A child was usually fed a little of whatever the family had to eat. This process started as soon as the child began to walk, and by the time he could run alone weaning was completed. The lack of proper feeding at this period, particularly during the summer months, was partially responsible for a high infant mortality rate. Infants were not permitted to eat salt as it was thought to cause white sores on the tongue (Spier 1928).

RAISING SMALL CHILDREN

Children began to learn the skills and develop the abilities they would need later in life at an early age. Small children soon learned to swim. Boys learned to trap and shoot at an early age. When a boy was old enough, he would be taken on trips during which the father showed him how to do a variety of things. Progress was judged by the boy's accomplishments, and his maturity was linked to his hunting ability; for example, the boy could not smoke until he had killed a coyote. His father also taught him social responsibilities. Girls were trained by their mothers in various household tasks, and both boys and girls were brought up to listen to the chiefs, who, from time to time, gave moral lectures to the group as a whole.

A boy was frequently urged to run toward the rising sun, carrying a coil of cedar bark lighted at one end (the so-called "slow match"). When he had reached the limit of his strength he stopped and rubbed the glowing end of the bark into his ankles, knees, wrists, and elbows to keep from becoming rheumatic. He threw the coil of bark over his head, turned to pick it up, and ran home. This taught him not to go far from camp before remembering a forgotten article. Training in running was important, both for hunting and to fulfill social responsibilities. A boy continued to run throughout much of his early life in training situations, while actually moving from area to area, in hunting, and, of course, in races. A man also ran during his wife's menstrual periods (Spier 1928).

The girl's first menstruation was important. At dawn on each day of the first menses, she, too, had to run towards the sun, though the distance was much shorter than that expected from the boy. Like the boy, she carried the slow match. Her body was washed with yucca root suds and painted red, and her face was decorated with brown cactus juice. While she ran, stones, heated in the fire, were buried under moist sand or earth and covered with leaves and brush and blankets. When she returned the girl lay on this warm bed, protected by a shade. She was allowed to eat little and could scratch herself only with a stick or deer tibia. An old woman sat beside her, giving her moral instructions. This whole ritual continued for four days, during which she was not allowed to sleep. Eating meat during menstruation was thought to cause barrenness (Spier 1928). The taboos against meat and against scratching with the fingers continued in force throughout subsequent menstruations. Sexual intercourse during menstruation was also taboo (Spier 1928).

Children's names were frequently acquired after they began to develop their own personalities. There were no formal names. Adult nicknames were customarily acquired as the result of some embarrassing situation, often at the time of marriage. School teachers and nurses had to keep records, so by 1941 English names were given at a relatively early age.

Instances have been reported of indifference and failure to care for babies, and there was a constant theme in stories of the child who died because it was not wanted. This rejection, it was said, might even be the cause of suicide.

Medicines for children were essentially the same as those for adults. They were often given in weaker doses, and only the milder remedies were used.

ADULT HEALTH CARE

To some extent the general health of the entire group was enhanced by group dances and by prayers made by the chiefs. The sweat bath, though not primarily used for curing, was thought to have curative properties. Not much attention was given to medical practices, but the average Havasupai household had someone in it who was moderately familiar with herbal remedies and could take care of the ordinary, everyday illnesses that the family might have. Table 8.3 shows plants used in medical treatments. Many of the remedies were relatively simple, direct applications of medicinal materials for curing or protecting.

Ant bites were treated by rubbing a folded leaf of jimson weed over them. Bee stings were rubbed with salt. Pinyon gum was put on cuts or wounds of both people and animals. Skin rashes were washed with suds made with saltbush leaves. This remedy was also good for the treatment of chicken pox, or as E.U. insisted upon calling it, "a measel." A decoction of sagebrush was good for sores or pimples.

An irritation in the throat was sometimes cured by chewing arrowweed leaves or drinking a decoction made from them. There were a number of teas, some of them used as regular drinks, which were thought to have some medicinal values.

TABLE 8.3
Plants Used in Medicine

Scientific Name	Common Name
Aloysia wrightii	Wright lippa
Artemisia ludoviciana	wormwood, sagebrush
Artemisia tridentata	sagebrush
Atriplex canescens	saltbush
Berberis repens	Oregon-grape
Cowania mexicana	cliff-rose
Datura metaloides	jimson weed
Ephedra viridis	Mormon tea
Eriogonum corymbosum	wild buckwheat
Juniperus osteosperma	juniper
Leucelene ericoides	white aster
Phlox spp.	phlox
Pinus edulis	pinyon
Porophyllum gracile	odora
Ptelea pallida	hop tree
Swertia radiata	deers-ears
Tessaria sericea	arrowweed
Thamnosma montana	turpentine broom
Tridens pulchellus	fluff grass

Lippa and wild buckwheat were thought to help a headache and ease rheumatic pains. Mormon tea, particularly, was used to clean the bowels.

Colds, coughs, and headaches resulting from a cold were treated with juniper. The common sagebrush was also helpful; leafy stems were placed on coals so that the fumes could be inhaled for a cold. The fresh leaves might be chewed for a cough. More often the leaves were pounded, boiled in water for ten to fifteen minutes, and allowed to cool. The usual dose of this sagebrush brew was a cupful before breakfast and again after supper for two or three days. Other authorities specified two tablespoons every half hour or hour for one day.

For a particularly bad cold or stomachache, there was a well-known combination of juniper, sagebrush, cliff rose, and an unidentified plant (*akwathika*). A medicine man who particularly advocated its use told of administering this concoction to a white visitor who had become ill. The patient recovered rapidly and presented the medicine man with four dollars. The medicine man's comment, in retrospect, was enlightening: he stated that his patient wasn't a white man—he was a gentleman!

Minor stomach troubles were treated with a variety of herbs. Mormon tea and fluff-grass tea were used in mild cases. A mild medicine which was used for babies, as well as for adults, was brewed from *Leucelene ericoides*, or the little, wild phlox. The root was pounded on a rock, boiled for five or ten minutes, and allowed to cool. The dose was half a cup, to be rubbed all over the body or on the stomach. Apparently, stronger medicines were brewed from other herbs, and with these, too, a decoction might be rubbed onto the stomach or over the entire body. Oregon-grape, known as "Coyote's medicine," was often collected and the roots stored for future use as a stomachache medicine. The roots were boiled for two or three hours, allowed to cool, and the liquid was drunk three times a day. If this remedy was to be given to babies, the root was peeled first and the resulting tea was diluted with water, because it was a strong medicine with laxative powers.

Leaves of the evil-smelling turpentine broom (the Havasupai name means "rat stomach") might be pounded and then rubbed onto a hurting abdomen or made into a tea either by soaking the plant in cold water or boiling it for three to fifteen minutes. This tea was very bitter, and was strong medicine; a cupful would cause vomiting or act as a laxative within two hours. (Rat feces were similarly employed.) The related and equally smelly hop tree ("deer stomach") was used externally only. The leaves were boiled in water and the resulting liquid rubbed on a child's abdomen. Since herbs were used in the sweat bath, some Havasupai thought it might be a good idea to use this plant, too. However, it caused the bathers' cheeks to swell up; this experiment was not repeated.

Another highly scented herb, *Porophyllum gracile* (the Havasupai name means "Chuckwalla eats") was a well-known medicine used primarily against pain or aches, including abdominal pains. It was prepared by pounding the leaves and placing them in water; the mixture might be boiled, but not necessarily. The resulting liquid could be used as a wash on a sore or rubbed on the skin as a liniment; the liquid might be drunk, though this was less common. The crushed herb was sometimes rubbed directly on the skin, "so that the smell will go in."

Deers-ears, known to the Havasupai as "wolf's medicine," is a tall plant with a deep, thick root which grows in yellow-pine country. The root was an important medicine. Before it could be dug, a speech had to be made to the plant telling it what a good medicine it was and that its help was needed. The entire root was boiled for five minutes and the resulting liquid cooled by adding cold water. A drink was taken of this liquid first thing in the morning and again at night. It was said to be good for digestive upsets, colds, and similar troubles. Taken in conjunction with a sweat bath, it was recommended for gonorrhea.

9. Keeping Things Organized

Among the Havasupai, as elsewhere, successful living came through organization. The people marshalled their resources, understood their needs, and—operating through established channels—balanced the one against the other. Various daily activities, as well as certain special events, were organized and carried out by specific social units within the tribe (Table 9.1). By the time a man had married and acquired a family, he was already aware of the established channels whereby food was obtained and distributed. He hunted and gave away meat and later received meat from others. His wife gathered for the family and did most of the cooking. He cleared the land and irrigated it; together they planted and harvested the crop; she prepared most of the food for storage. After the Spanish came to the Southwest, the man looked after the horses and the cattle, if there were any. Similar routines were established for other activities. Men cut, hauled, and erected the heavy timbers, while the women worked on the thatch of the houses. The man hunted, skinned, and tanned animal hides and made the leather clothing. Within recent times the sewing of cloth clothing has been carried out by the women.

COUNTING AND ORGANIZING TIME

There were time guides to behavior which people needed to know. They had to know the proper season to plant, when to water, and when to harvest. They had to know when floods might come and when to hold dances. A man needed to know where and when game animals were to be found. Much of this organization required enumeration and counting. The type of counting involved in gambling was simple and known to all. The concept of fractions was totally unknown, although there was a vague term for "half" or "middle" or "in between." Keeping track of counts consisted of keeping track of things, things that in themselves did not matter—marks on the wall, short sticks, lengths of narrow-leaved yucca, or knots in a cord of string, with one to be cut off each night until "the" day finally arrived. One did not count time, one counted events instead: "After so many nights...," or "He has seen so many winters."

The position of the sun during the day was sharply segmented, and appointments were often made in terms of the sun's position. Similarly, the positions of shadows were also used (e.g., "When the shadow of the cliffs reaches the river"). Time divisions within the year were determined by observing the apparent movements of the sun from its southern position during the winter solstice to the northern position at the summer solstice. These divisions were noted with relative ease by a series of observations from a fixed point to a point on the horizon at which the sun rose. Such a system necessitated permanent residence in one area during the period of observation and repeated observation from year to year from that same point. The solstices, of course, can be recognized during a short period of observation, but any subdivision of the time between these requires a fixed and continual, year-after-year observation from one point. This system of observation is complicated, involves a good deal of care, and suggests at least some kind of a method of keeping track of numbers.

The semi-nomadic way of life which the Havasupai lived during much of the year did not encourage an extensive amount of solar observation, but during the period when they were more or less constantly in residence within the valley (from spring through early fall), the rudiments of such a system were in active use. Observations were made by many of

TABLE 9.1
Activities Organized and Carried Out by Various Social Units

Activity	Individual	Immediate Family	Field Band	Blood Kin	Neighborhood	Tribe	Chiefs	Shamans	Singers
Flow of consumable goods									
Daily needs		X							
Gathering		X	X						
Small game	X	X	X			X (Men)			
Large game	X		X			X (Men)	X	X	
Agriculture		X							
Agricultural dams					X		X		
Goods consumed or traded									
Buckskin	X								
Basketry	X								
Pottery	X								
Salt					X		X		
Red paint					X		X		
House Building		X							
Emergencies									
Drought								X	

the people, but the chiefs were particularly concerned and watched with more care than did the others. Each observer had a fixed point of observation which was used year after year. As with the stars, it was the point of the sun's rising which was significant. Although the solstices were watched, they were not considered especially significant. Observations on the position of the sun were made at approximately one-week intervals, and certain points on the horizon were remembered as significant

TABLE 9.1
(continued)

Activity	Individual	Immediate Family	Field Band	Blood Kin	Neighborhood	Tribe	Chiefs	Shamans	Singers
Emergencies (*continued*)									
Illness: minor	X	X							
major								X	
War: defense						X	X		
offense						X (Men)	X		
Crime		X							
Dances						X	X		X
Status Change Birth		X							
Marriage			X				X		
Death			X			X	X		
New chiefs			X			X			
Group knowledge (calendar, morals, myths)							X		X
Foreign Contact	X						X		
Trail Maintenance	X					X (Men)	X		

for certain activities, particularly in the agricultural cycle. Once the sun had reached a given point, it might then be necessary to count a given number of days.

The Seasons

The Havasupai seemed to think in terms of three seasonal divisions of the year. The cold season (winter) was called *acutika*. The term for spring, *nyimuwaimima*, contained the word for warm (*muwai*), as did the names of the months for the "warm" period. The terms for the summer months and for summer itself, *'inya-tuya*, were based upon the word for sun, *'inyaa'a*.

One is tempted to recognize in the data a fourth period, corresponding to fall. References to it, however, do not seem to be clear. This period, *matikamai* or *matmunima*, was described as coming "when all the stars have come up and are gone and there is nothing to tell the season by." This would certainly not be the fall season. Two informants insisted that there were only three seasons. The inclusion of *matikamai* within the list of seasons, therefore, would not be reliable, though it is possible that the term does have reference to a specific portion of the year.

Some periods of time within the year were told by the changing face of nature (e.g., when the cottonwood sheds its fluffy seeds it is time to plant), and the organization of events within the Havasupai year was centered around the appearance of certain stars just before sunrise and the phases of the moon.

The Lunar Cycle

The Havasupai counted more than twelve and less than thirteen lunar months in a solar year (Table 9.2). Since the solar year determined the seasons and, hence, the economic cycle, it took precedence over the lunar cycle. Nevertheless, it was upon the basis of the waxing and waning of the moon that the solar year was subdivided. In general, the Havasupai, like other humans without a fixed day-count, did not attempt the impossible. As Spier (1928) stated, "These Indians are interested only in designating a series of periods without attempting to fix their limits, and these periods are roughly lunations, the names of which are variable and frequently in doubt."

During the spring and early summer, while the Havasupai were residing in the canyon, they made highly specific observations of the season by watching the point on the horizon at which the sun rose. During this solar observation period it was not essential that the lunar calendar be maintained with

TABLE 9.2
Havasupai Lunar Calendar

Equivalent Month	Associated Star Cluster	Havasupai Name for the Time Period	English Translation of Time Period
August(?)	Leo ("Hand")	*sal'ciola*	Hand rises[1,3]
September(?)	(none)	*kavo-tavo'ooka*	Storm ends[2]
		kavo-tova'oma	Storm ends[3]
October– November	Corona ("Hoop")*	*hala'apa'kinueeva*	Man in the moon shut up in his house[1,2,3]
December	Scorpio ("Pole")	*'i'pe'ca'alai*	Pole rises[1]
		kavo-tuviaka	Storm middle[2]
		hine	Pole[3]
January	Altair, Aquila ("Cold Star")	*hamasi'katati'a*	Star man named *hate'u'u'*[1,2]
		celqa'loya	Feces interrupted (refers to myth of Altair)[3]
February	(none)	*muwai-puk*	Warm begins[1,2,3]
March	(none)	*muwai-tuviaka*	Warm middle[1,2,3]
April	(none)	*muwai-tavo'ok*	Warm ends[1,2,3]
May	(none)	*'inyata-puk*	Hot begins[1,2,3]
May–June	(none)	*'inyaka-tutumiyaka*	Hot middle[1]
		'inya-tuyahana	– – –[2]
		'inya-toviaka	Hot middle[3]
June	Hyades ("Rabbits"?)	*kavo-casapeka*	Storm part way[1,2]
		'inyata-vo'oma	Hot ends[3]
July	Orion ("Mountain Sheep")	*kavo-puk-ciwuk*	Storm begins[1]
		kavo-pawaca	Storm ____?[2]
		kovo-puk	Storm begins[3]
July–August	(none)	*kovo-tuviak*	Storm middle[3]

*Listed by Whiting, with the notation that the Havasupai considered it "not significant."
[1]Spier's (1928) Havasupai list
[2]List by a Havasupai elder
[3]Kroeber's (1935) Walapai list

accuracy. During the late fall and winter months there was no great need for critical timing, and the rather vague lunar months were adequate to the needs of the Havasupai. Most of the lunations during this period were identified by the star cluster which made its first appearance during that lunar cycle.

Although about half of the lunar months were associated with certain star clusters, only a few actually derived their

TABLE 9.3
Alternate Calendar Terms

Phase Within Season	Description of Season		
	Warm Season *muwai-* "warm"	Hot Season *'inyata-* "hot"	Storm Season *kavo-* "storm"
-puk "begins"	*muwai-puk* "warm begins"	*'inyata-puk* "hot begins"	*kavo-puk* "storm begins"
-tuviaka "middle"	*muwai-tuviaka* "warm middle"	*'inya-tuviaka* "hot middle"	*kavo-tuviaka* "storm middle"
-tova'o "ends"	*muwai-tova'ok* "warm ends"	*'inya-tova'oma* "hot ends"	*kavo-tova'oma* "storm ends"

names from these constellations. There was a separate series of names, which—had it been used in its entirety—would have provided nine month names. Table 9.3 shows the nature of these terms.

From the confused and limited data at hand in 1941 it was impossible to say with certainty when the year began. The month counts which have been collected apparently began with the current month at the time of the interview. Spier (1928) stated that the year began with the rising of the "hoop" constellation, which he said marked the month *sal-ciola* in early November. The "hoop," which does rise in November, was confused by Spier or his informants with *sal*, "the hand," which rises in late August. The latter coincides with the harvest festival, which was the culmination of the year, and would, therefore, also mark the beginning of Havasupai attention to the lunar (rather than the solar) cycle. The harvest festival would be a natural place to break the year, and, until some more reliable data appear, late August or early September should be assumed as the beginning of the year.

It is interesting to note that the Havasupai had at their disposal the techniques and knowledge by which they could have evolved a calendrical system like that of the great centers in Middle America. That time counts were limited to relatively short periods reflects the interests and demands of their relatively simple life, rather than the limitations of their powers of observation. They were aware of the basic inconsistencies in astronomical cycles, the disharmony between the solar and the lunar cycles, the difference between the movable and the fixed stars, and the variability of weather cycles. Their failure to explore these or to keep records must, therefore, be attributed to a lack of interest.

ORGANIZING THE USE OF LAND

To live in this area, by Havasupai standards, the family had to have farmland. There was little for sale and less that could be cleared, so if one did not inherit land he virtually had to leave the tribe. The ways of inheriting land were clearly defined. The ownership of the agricultural land and the techniques by which it changed hands have been described in considerable detail by Spier (1928) and Service (1947) and will only be summarized here. The main characteristics were that land passed from father to son in the male line when there were male descendants who could use it. Daughters and widows retained the right to use land, but they did not thereby obtain the right to pass it on to their children, unless there were no male relatives who could claim it. Unused land which had been abandoned could be cleared by anyone, including non-Havasupai who married into the tribe. The produce of the land (cultivated crops, including fruit trees) was owned separately from the land, and was the property of whoever tended the crop that growing season.

The ownership of non-agricultural land was not as carefully defined. Sources of water—springs, tanks, and water holes—rather than land areas, were considered the property of particular individuals. They were inherited and sold much as was the agricultural land. The ownership of such water sources consisted of responsibility for the maintenance of the dam or cleaning out of the spring or tank, but did not exclude others from using the water or from temporarily camping near it. The range of the group must have been sufficiently large that there was relatively little conflict over the ownership of such areas.

Pasture land on the Plateau and the Esplanade was inherited in a similar manner. "Those that use the land own it, and their sons inherit it." The Esplanade pastures were normally inherited as a unit and were used exclusively by one man or a group of related men. The development of this organizational pattern seems to have taken place entirely within the native society. It could not have derived directly from Euro-American culture, since the land in question was part of the Grand Canyon National Park and could not be legally owned by the Indians. The rights of ownership, if indeed that term may be applied at all, rest completely upon native sanctions and, therefore, must have developed within Havasupai culture.

CONTROLLING THE SPIRITS—SHAMANS

Shamans were men who had special knowledge and powers that enabled them to do things that were beyond the ability of the ordinary individual. The basis of their specialized techniques was the control of an abstract power or spirit.

A man's dreams about animals or spirits were important because they might give him power. If he was one of those who had the strength of personality to use his power single-handed against the spirits, or against the community, he became a shaman. Some shamans had special powers for curing, some for hunting, and others for controlling the weather.

The Havasupai believed that disease might be caused by the presence of a spirit in the body of a patient. It might be the spirit of a hawk which the child's mother heard calling while she was pregnant or the spirit of a mountain lion who had contaminated meat eaten by the father. It might be the spirit of a dead Navajo shaman who objected to the way someone was singing his personal songs or the spirit of a dead Havasupai shaman, coming for the soul of his great-grandson. It might be the Great Spirit who made the deer, angry at a man for having killed more deer than he could eat (Spier 1928).

These spirits had to be met with a similar force—another spirit. So the man who would cure others of disease caused by

A Havasupai shaman, around the end of the nineteenth century. Photo by George Wharton James, ca. 1899; courtesy of Southwest Museum.

spirits must himself be able to control a spirit. A shaman had control over such a spirit, usually that of a wolf or one of the other mythological animals. The shaman's spirit was acquired in dreams. It took time to get a spirit, but when such a spirit came it entered the body of the shaman, talked to him in his sleep, and instructed him. Later, after much practice and dreaming, the individual began to effect cures, and it was this spirit which was called through the songs which the shaman had learned. Upon being called by the shaman, this spirit entered into the body of the patient. It surveyed the situation, sometimes argued with the resident spirit, and, if it was able to force the alien spirit to leave the patient, a cure was effected.

Most spirits were not in themselves either good or evil. The shaman might use his spirit to help others, as in curing, or he might use it to cause disease or to kill people. The choice of how the power was to be used rested with the shaman. When there was an epidemic, the people often suspected that the local shaman was causing it. If this thought became a strong conviction, the shaman might be killed (Spier 1928). Thus, being a shaman involved some risk: if too many of his patients died or there was an epidemic, he might lose his own life. On the other hand, such a position had its attractive aspects: a shaman was respected, feared, and considered to be an important person in the group. In addition, his practice, though arduous and time-consuming, often provided an element of wealth.

When called on a case, the curing-shaman ordinarily sang over the patient for four nights, accompanying himself with a gourd rattle (the gourd seeds were obtained from the Hopi). Often it was enough that the shaman sang by himself. In difficult cases, however, he called for others to come and help him sing. The social pressure of the group singing seems to have been more effective than that of the shaman by himself.

There was some specialization in the curing of disease. Different men had power which helped them cure wounds, fractures, toothache, or stomach ailments in children. There were also specialists who were concerned with snakes. Like the routine general practitioners, snake-shamans also had a considerable body of practical knowledge at hand. A snake bite was treated by such men by cutting open the wound and sucking out the poison. Whenever possible, the limb would be tied above the wound to prevent the movement of the poison to the body. A ring of sagebrush might be put around the limb since this herb was associated with snakes.

Throughout this area tribal curing-shamans sometimes came together in a public demonstration of their powers. There was a good deal of sleight of hand and showmanship in these affairs. Success in one of these inter-tribal medical conventions did much to improve one's reputation. It is not certain that the Havasupai participated in these, but they may have been well aware of such activities.

Snake shamans certainly indulged in a bit of showmanship when demonstrating their power to handle snakes. One shaman, for example, used to pin down a rattlesnake by putting the end of his walking stick just behind the snake's head. He then picked up the reptile by the head and tail and pulled it taut; children said he "turned it into a stick."

Spier (1928) expressed some doubt about whether snake shamans were to be equated with the general shamans who cure. Discussions in 1941 revealed that they certainly performed in similar fashion: they both sucked foreign matter caused by spirit-animals; they both sang and used a gourd rattle; they both used a certain amount of practical medical knowledge. In addition, the use of certain herbs by both types of shamans was dictated by associations with animals, and the public show of the snake shaman was to be equated to the public displays of the general practitioners. That Snake himself was a malevolent character seems to be only incidental: the shaman worked against Snake, rather than with him, but he definitely had power over his spirit.

In addition to curing-shamans, there were those who dreamed of deer and were able to draw near without scaring them. Such shamans were excellent hunters. Other men dreamed of clouds and hail and rain and learned to sing weather songs. Such men, called weather shamans, played much the same social role as did the curing shamans. They, too, could use their power for good or for evil. The last weather shaman (died ca. 1928)* seems to have been rather a remarkable individual, and it is difficult to tell which of his many activities were the result of his status as a weather shaman and which were the result of his own driving personality. It is apparent that such men were expected to be able to bring rain when it was needed. This man was instrumental in developing imitations of Hopi rain rituals and was a strong influence within the tribe during the time he was alive. He is credited with causing a flood by singing rain songs in the sweat lodge.

LEADING THE TRIBE—CHIEFS

The young married man was only too acutely aware of the fact that the chiefs were concerned with the "proper" nature of his marriage. Through the talks of the chiefs, a moral code and a whole set of ideals had been brought to his attention again and again. It was the chiefs who were constantly urging the people to do the right thing at the right time. It was the chiefs who, more than anyone else, watched the sun and the moon and the stars. The young man was also aware that it was the chiefs who called upon him to join in work projects, not only for dams, but also for working on the trails. It was under one of the chiefs that he played his part in defending the village, and, should he feel like going on a raid against the enemy, it, too, must be organized and approved by a chief.

---

* Whiting had a rather personal encounter with the residual power of the last weather shaman in the spring of 1950. Although it was disrespectful and dangerous to speak of the dead, Whiting ventured to inquire about him one bright day in May while he was talking with some of the Havasupai near Grand Canyon Village. There was some reluctance to discuss him. He had been a powerful man and if he was disturbed he could still cause storms. Nevertheless, they did tell Whiting what he wanted to know. The following morning the South Rim of the Grand Canyon was blanketed with several inches of snow, and Whiting's Havasupai informants felt that they had talked a little too much the day before.

It was a chief that a foreign visitor first went to see upon arrival in the community. The young man also knew that it was to these men that he could go when he was in trouble or in need of advice. It was these men who knew how to talk and to whom the group would listen. And he knew that any man could become a chief.

But to become a chief one must first become a good man, an able leader, and something of an orator. He must know the ways of earning a living. If he was brave in war, a good worker, an excellent provider, knew all the proper prayers, if he talked well, and if the people listened to him, then he might be accepted as one of the chiefs, one of the leaders of his people. These traits were important and often took much training, so it is not surprising that the chieftainship often passed from father to son. But this was not always the case: there were those sons of chiefs to whom the people would not listen, and whom they would not choose as a chief. There were also men who were not sons or grandsons of chiefs, yet they had become chiefs.

A chief did not "hold office." He had influence but no formal power; he organized, but gave no orders. He felt responsible for the welfare of his many "children," but he was not responsible for their behavior. He was only "the one who was chosen," "the one who was superlatively good," "the leader of his children." If a chief was outstanding among those leaders who had been chosen, he might be called the "big chief," recognized as the head man of the tribe. The power of the chiefs lay in their ability to organize, interpret, and adapt the values of traditional Havasupai society through persuasion, and this ability was recognized as being of great value to the individual and to the entire group.

ACQUIRING INDIVIDUAL STATUS

For the most part the inheritance of land, the planting of crops, and the watching of the seasons were family affairs. The distribution of fresh meat and the building of irrigation dams involved working with other family units. At marriage a young man established close relationships with another family group and his obligations began to broaden, but he still remained a good deal of an individualist. As such, there were several roles he could attempt to achieve special status in society. As described above, he might become a shaman or a chief, or he might be a singer or a warrior. If one learned a song in a dream, it had to be sung immediately on awakening or it would be lost. Songs had power, and since a man's songs were his property, they brought him individual status. Others might sing with him, but once he was dead his songs were rarely sung because he might be quite angry if they were sung improperly. During his lifetime the man with songs was a welcome individual. He led the singing for the dance festivals and sometimes developed new song-rituals of his own. He might also be called upon to sing with a shaman during a curing ceremony. Songs might be sung whenever the group was together, and he who had songs to sing was considered a valuable member of the community.

At one time the man who did not acquire power through dreams used to be able to gain a reputation as a warrior. By 1941 athletic prowess had replaced warrior ability as a way to gain individual status. At this time the cowboy occupied an enviable role in Havasupai society, and many a young man lived from one rodeo to the next.

10. Indians in a Changing World

In traditional Havasupai culture, as a man got older he let other, younger men do the running. He moved more slowly, with more dignity, and, with rheumatism, more painfully. If he had a family and was wise and influential as a leader, he was respected and well taken care of. If not, the chiefs saw to it that someone at least provided for his physical needs.

To such men in 1941 came memories of the past and doubts for the future. They had time for reflection and evaluation, "Where," they asked, "does it get you?" Death for the individual, of course, but of the others who would be left behind? What was it all coming to?

CHANGES IN DEATH CUSTOMS

Like the man who loses at gambling, a man does not often die all at once. Of course, it did happen; one cannot ride gloriously—hell bent for leather, steal horses and women from touchy neighbors, go on long trips, hunt large animals with a bow and arrow at close range, or fight in a white man's war without risk. Then, too, there were the dangers of the night, when ghosts and evil spirits were abroad. In addition, the white man had introduced diseases that brought rashes and death for children (measles and pneumonia) and others that slowly but surely ate out the insides of a man (tuberculosis, gonorrhea, and, occasionally, syphilis). Even if a person escaped all these dangers, his spirit was eventually claimed by old age. When a person died, it was essential to do two things: remove the body and readjust society. In 1941 the Havasupai were changing their ideas about how these things should be done.

Burial Replaces Cremation

The traditional method of disposing of the dead among the Yuman-speaking relatives of the Havasupai was based upon the fear that a person's ghost could cause sickness or death. Consequently everything must be done to remove the dead, his belongings, and anything that would cause people to remember or speak of him (thus causing his spirit to return). The funeral was based upon the destructive and purifying power of the fire. The Havasupai shared this belief and followed similar practices.

At the time of death the body and the personal belongings of the dead person were burned. What could not be burned with the body, such as the house, was burned separately, and what could not be burned at all was destroyed; among the Havasupai, horses were killed and standing crops and fruit trees were cut down. Individuals who had been contaminated by attending the body took off their clothes and placed these on the funeral pyre and observed other precautions, such as washing or going without salt or meat for a designated period. Since a man's songs were his property and belonged strictly to him, they were sung at his funeral (Spier 1933, Kroeber 1935). Likewise the deeds which made a great warrior famous were part of his reputation and must be retold, or re-enacted (Spier 1933).

During the last decade of the nineteenth century, pressure from Indian agents was being applied upon the Havasupai to abandon cremation (James 1900). Although occasional cremations did occur after this time (e.g., Rock Jones in the late 1920s), by 1904 cremation was no longer the customary form of disposal of the dead among the Havasupai (Spier 1928). The pressure to substitute burial for cremation was partly due to

Christian opposition, based on the effects that burning the body might have on resurrection. However, religious opposition was not the only issue: it was difficult to see how a group of poverty-stricken Indians could ever better their economic condition if, upon the death of a man or woman, all that individual's property was destroyed.

Under earlier conditions, the cremation system undoubtedly worked fairly well for Havasupai society, since a man's property did not include much beyond his immediate tools and his clothing. The land could not be destroyed. The crops might be cut down, but that was a minor item over a period of years. The loss of a crude hut, some clothing, a bundle of arrows and a bow and quiver, a stone knife, several game counters—this was no threat to the social or economic life of the aboriginal community. In addition, the removal of the personal belongings helped to remove the memory of the deceased. Without items which characterized an individual, those who were left were not constantly reminded of him. They were offered less opportunity to speak his name and thus call him back, which would make him lonesome and desire to take one of the living with him for company on the long road which a man enters at death.

A modern Havasupai owned one or more horses, some cattle, an orchard, an elaborate frame house, a car, and a good supply of household equipment. To burn or destroy all of these items in order to get rid of a ghost made that ghost somewhat expensive. When friends and relatives burned clothing which had been purchased with hard-earned cash, such a performance took on an economic aspect which loomed large in the minds of those who sought to promote the well-being of the society. The cure for this situation, as these people saw it in the late nineteenth century, was that the Havasupai should substitute burial for cremation.

The Mourning Ritual

The change from a funeral involving cremation to one involving burial was forced upon traditional Havasupai society by outside pressures, and the adaptation involved the transportation of the body a considerable distance from the village for burial. The group as a whole, therefore, could not follow the body to the grave. The feelings of group solidarity which were formerly expressed at the cremation now began to find expression in a mourning ritual, which was learned from the neighboring tribes.

About 1880 the Mohave invited some of their Walapai friends to a mourning ritual. The Walapai were much impressed, and when they went home they decided to have a mourning ritual of their own. They learned some Yuman songs from the Mohave and learned still more songs from the Chemehuevi, a Paiute group living near the Mohave.

Some years after the Walapai had absorbed the pattern from the Mohave, some Havasupai were invited to participate in the mourning rituals of the Walapai (Spier 1928). They, in turn, went home and began to duplicate the new rituals among their own people. They learned the new dance pattern and the songs without much trouble, even though the words, which were in Mohave or Paiute, were unintelligible to them. The Walapai eventually adapted their mourning ritual into an annual holiday (Kroeber 1935), and, under the sponsorship of an aggressive leader named Captain Jim, the Havasupai undertook to present this new ritual at one of the annual harvest dances. The idea was not well received by the spectators, however, since they knew that these songs were associated with the dead and were, therefore, inappropriate for a harvest festival. In 1941 these dances were performed and the songs were sung only where the Havasupai felt they were appropriate: at mourning rituals held soon after the death of a tribal member. The Havasupai often invited the Walapai or even the Mohave to come and help them sing. On these occasions the group gathered to talk about the dead person (with no fear of the ghost). Presents were burned or put into the coffin (clothing for adults, canned milk for babies). The Havasupai and the Walapai both seem to have absorbed the Yuma-Mohave mourning ritual as a compensation for the loss of certain aspects of their culture which resulted from the substitution of burial for cremation.

THE GHOST DANCE

The Havasupai in 1941 did not want to go back to their old ways. Their culture had mingled with too many other cultures for them to ever resume a purely Indian way of life. But there was a time, when these cultural streams first met, that the Havasupai tried to turn back the clock. There is little to document the changes in the culture that went on during the ten years which followed the 1880 discovery of mineral deposits (especially lead) below the village. It takes no great exercise of the imagination to realize what must have happened with the sudden influx of prospectors, explorers, newspaper reporters, miners, surveyors, ethnologists, tourists, and just plain adventurers who visited the canyon in the years immediately after the discovery of these deposits. Neighboring Indian groups were likewise feeling the effects of the Euro-American encroachment and throughout the Indian populations of northern Arizona there was a feeling of upset and of change. They all faced the future with a certain amount of fear and uncertainty. The Hopi, who had been wrestling with the problem for several centuries, were better able to cope with the effects of these events. But the Havasupai, long sheltered from direct contact with whites, now felt the changes more keenly than the rest.

Unstable conditions in traditional Indian cultures were not peculiar to northern Arizona. As Euro-American frontiers moved in upon them after the close of the Civil War, many Indian peoples throughout the western portion of the United States were upset and troubled, and, as a result, a messianic cult called the Ghost Dance spread far and wide among Indian groups. The basic doctrine of this cult stated that in the near future the dead were to return, the white man was going to disappear, game would again be plentiful, and prosperity and security for the Indian populations would be restored. In the meantime, those who were to become part of this future life must join the movement, participate in the dances, and wear a white costume. The exact form and nature of the movement varied somewhat throughout the country, but at heart it was an anti-white movement seeking escape from conditions beyond the control of native minority groups (see Dobyns and Euler [1967] for a thorough discussion of the Ghost Dance cult).

In 1889 word reached the Havasupai and the Walapai that something was happening among the Paiutes to the north. A delegation of Walapai and Havasupai journeyed to St. George, Utah, and learned of the Ghost Dance from a Paiute there. Under the guidance of a Walapai shaman named Jeff, this Paiute visited the Walapai to explain the meaning of the cult. From the start, some of the Walapai remained skeptical, but many Walapai and some of the Havasupai (including the chief who had been active in securing U.S. government approval of the Havasupai reservation) became interested in the movement. They learned the Paiute songs and began to encourage people to dance. Later they added additional songs that Jeff learned in dreams (Kroeber 1935; Stephen 1936).

The dance form itself was a modification of the familiar circle dance. Men and women danced around a center pole, as in the scalp dance, but on the top of the pole there were feathers instead of scalps. As many of the dancers as possible were dressed in white. There was considerable emphasis upon purification by washing which was reminiscent of part of the old death rituals.

Men climbed the center pole and clung there until exhausted, then slid to the ground insensible. Upon recovering, they said they had been visiting with the dead. An account of a visitor in 1895 describes the Havasupai dancing in a circle around a pole at the top of which was some "medicine." Dancers fell exhausted and were removed from the circle (Arizona Graphic 1899). George Wharton James (1900) tells of a Chemehuevi evangelist and hysterical women dancers who became unconscious. A less reliable reference to hysterical shouting, leaping, and women dancers who became exhausted and were dragged from the dance circle was given by Dama Margaret Smith who visited the Havasupai about 1923 (D.M. Smith 1923).

As time went by, skepticism increased among the Walapai. The dead did not return, and food stores began to disappear. Under these conditions the enthusiasm which Jeff still displayed could not prevail and the dancers went home. Enthusiasm seemed to have passed even more rapidly among the Havasupai. When the men who had contacted the dead during the dance themselves began to die, the initial popularity of the movement quickly evaporated. The movement as an integrated whole lasted only a short time among the Havasupai (Spier 1928); it must have had, nevertheless, a tremendous effect upon individuals within the group and left its mark on the thinking and personalities of some of them for many years.

ADAPTATIONS IN BASKET-MAKING TRADITIONS

As outside pressures moved closer and closer, it was clear to the Havasupai that they could not go back, even though their cultural identity as Indians was at stake. Many of the old ways were being abandoned for something new and better: metal knives, guns, cooking pots that did not break, cloth clothing that could be washed clean of dirt and body odor, matches, horses, and cattle were all welcome and chosen additions to the Havasupai way of life. But pressure from whites also forced some unwanted changes, such as burial instead of cremation. It often seemed that everything that was old and familiar was "wrong." Throughout the country the doctrine that the only good Indian was a dead Indian had been preached for so long that the only Indian tradition which was approved by the whites was the artistic one. So the Indians ended up selling their art work; for the Havasupai this meant baskets.

In traditional Havasupai culture, baskets were one of the most important types of utensils. Of the two basic techniques used to make baskets, coiling and twining, the latter was by far the more common. Twined basketry included conical carrying baskets; small, conical baskets; flat trays; large, bi-conical

TABLE 10.1
Plants Used in Twined Basketry

Scientific Name	Common Name
Basket Rims	
Amelanchier utahensis	service bush
Fallugia paradoxa	Apache plume
Prosopis juliflora	mesquite
Woven Elements	
Acacia gregii (strong)	catclaw
Populus fremontii (inferior)	cottonwood
Rhus trilobata (preferred)	squaw bush
Decoration	
Proboscidea spp.	devil's claws
Rhus trilobata	squaw bush

water jugs; and small, jug-shaped baskets. Coiled basketry was restricted apparently to vessels intended to hold water (for storage or for boiling food) and small cups. Plants used in twined and coiled basketry are shown in Tables 10.1 and 10.2.

While the introduction of new, decorative elements and of metal awls stimulated the production of Havasupai basketry, the real stimulus came from the Hopi. About 1890 the Hopi developed a passion for the decorated coil baskets of the Havasupai, perhaps because of the degeneration of their own basketry and the attitudes of the white collectors. Large numbers of the Havasupai coiled basket trays found in museums today were collected on the Hopi reservation during this period. There are accounts of Hopi women lining the interior walls of their houses with rows of these baskets (Mason 1902). Havasupai baskets also appeared in Hopi men's rituals on the antelope-snake altar (James 1903), and Hopi women inaugurated a modification of their traditional basket dance in which they imitated Havasupai costume and displayed Havasupai baskets (Fewkes 1899).

As Hopi interest began to wane in the early twentieth century, direct contact of the Havasupai with Anglo-Americans

TABLE 10.2
Plants Used in Coiled Basketry

Scientific Name	Common Name
Baccharis emoryi (rarely used)	groundsel tree
Chilopsis linearis (rarely used, for fill)	desert willow
Proboscidea spp.	devil's claws
Populus fremontii	cottonwood
Rhus trilobata (preferred)	squaw bush
Salix exigua (inferior)	coyote willow

began to become more common, and for many years their baskets found a ready market among tourists and National Park employees who lived near Grand Canyon Village. Traditional basket shapes and sizes were often modified to meet the needs of white purchasers. An innovative development in the late 1930s was the production of miniature baskets, only a fraction of an inch in diameter. These were ideal for those basket collectors who lived in trailers, but served no other useful function in either Havasupai or Euro-American culture.

By 1941 Havasupai basketry had become an uninspired artistic tradition. It had little color: only black and white materials were used. The designs were satisfactory, yet had no meaning, symbolically or artistically, for the Indians. They were nice baskets that were made by a nice group of housewives in their spare time. As many as could be made could be sold, but it was hard work, and it took a lot of time. There were many Havasupai women who said that what they got out of it did not make it worth the effort. For further discussion of Havasupai basketry, see McKee, McKee, and Herold (1975).

RELIGIOUS INFLUENCES FROM OTHER CULTURES

In the early twentieth century, as Euro-American and Indian cultures were colliding, the Havasupai began to be influenced by religious rituals from other cultures. At this time Christian missionaries had made some impact on the Havasupai, but the major influence in religious matters came from the Hopi.

The Ways of Borrowed Gods

The Havasupai knew the Hopi as a market for their red paint, buckskins, and baked mescal. They knew them as competitors in races, as the source of tools, pottery, blankets, drums, and many other goods. For them the Hopi were also a refuge, a knight's castle in a warring land, a source of seed and food, of shelter in winter, and of protection from hostile enemies. In the course of these contacts they also saw Hopi religion in action. They heard the prayers, watched the Hopi make and use prayer sticks and saw the Hopi gods dance. There, too, they laughed at the clowns who came with the dancers; their pantomime was at least understandable. All of these were wonderful things. Bit by bit the Havasupai brought these things home to their own valley and to their fields, including the prayers and the prayer sticks, which they deposited in their everflowing spring.

Under the leadership of one of the weather shamans, they tried the Hopi dances, using such textiles as they could afford to buy. They dressed themselves to look like the Hopi gods, but their simple crude masks were spotted with meaningless decorations. For the ruffs and skirts of green leaves they did not insist upon the Douglas fir, which the Hopi associated with the mountain homes of their gods, but used cottonwood instead. It looked just as pretty. They dressed themselves secretly in their own houses. They put on feathers, a white costume, and masks. As the men came out in single file, it was fun to watch, guessing who was who underneath all that disguise.

The dances seem to have varied considerably. Sometimes men and women dressed in white danced in a circle. The weather shaman who took so much interest in all of these dances made prayers for rain. That was as it should be. Dances always had been for the good of the community and for the rain that made the grass grow. They did not need rain for their fields, but they did need grass on the Plateau so that there would be wild seeds to collect and so that there would be food for the animals they wanted to hunt, and above all, so they could raise horses—horses to ride, horses to race. So they

*A Havasupai woman displays a basket made for sale.
Photo, c. 1941, from A. F. Whiting's files.*

danced for rain. They dressed themselves like the Hopi gods
and called themselves *"kaci'na"* (though it often sounded more
like *"gadjina"* to the Hopi ears).

While they danced, people began to talk, as people will.
Some of the Havasupai spoke a little Hopi, and eventually they
found out that the Hopi kachinas were the spirits of the dead. It
was a dangerous thing to call back the dead, but people went
on dancing. Then, in the dead of the winter, on January 1, 1910,
it happened. It rained, and rained again, and kept on raining.
The parched landscape drank what it could hold, but what it
could not hold began to run down the usually dry stream beds
and the river rose. Water began to pile up behind the earth
dams that the cattlemen had built until soon there was a small
lake in the middle of the desert. Eventually the earth dam gave
way and the water rushed through the Havasupai village with
the speed and indifference of an express train. It took the
school first. The agent crawled off the agency roof into the
limbs of a sheltering cottonwood as it took the agency building.
Most of the villagers made it to the talus slopes at the side of
the canyon as the village was wiped clean. Houses, orchards,
stoves, food, and an old grandmother went down, over the falls,
into oblivion. The falls themselves began to wear away, and the
river cut itself deeper into the valley floor.

After this the Havasupai thought twice about dancing for
rain. The shaman said it was a good thing, but others did not
agree. The Hopi, in their rock-bound villages high on the cliffs,
still danced for rain, but the Havasupai did not. The way of the
Hopi gods was not for them. These gods, however, left some of
their trappings behind. The clowns continued to entertain at
the harvest festival, brandishing whips and getting people to
dance, but no one dared pray openly and vigorously for rain.

Ritual of the Horse Song

After the adopted rituals of the Hopi gods were abandoned in
the second decade of the twentieth century, a Havasupai singer
dreamed a song about horses. From this song, the Havasupai

developed a ritual involving dances, songs, and prayers. Although the horse song belonged to a Havasupai singer, the complex ritual that grew out of it was heavily based on the Hopi kachina dances. It was performed in the afternoon and lasted several hours. The singers prepared in secret, apart from the dance area. As far as possible the men wore buckskin costumes and feathers. The bodies of the men, like those of the Hopi kachina dancers, were painted where they were exposed, and fingers were drawn through the paint to give a decorative effect. The horses were also painted, and fancy ribbons were attached to their bridles. The chief concern appears to have been disguise rather than decoration, for the markings on the horses were altered and the appearance of each man was so modified that he no longer looked like the same man.

When it was time to begin, the men mounted and rode into the dance area. They formed a line and began to sing to the accompaniment of the drum carried by the dreamer of songs. The first verse was primarily a prayer for the horses: that they should run without tiring, that they should never fall on the trail, that there would be rain in order that the horses might have grass to eat, that the horses should be good runners, and—of great importance in Havasupai thought—that these horses should win races.

At the end of this verse, the singers rode forward a short distance, dismounted, and formed a line in front of their horses. A second verse was then sung asking for the health of the riders and for help in raising good horses and plenty of children. The singers then mounted again and rode forward. The entire performance was repeated for a total of four verses.

There appear to have been several horse songs, all of which were modifications of this pattern, and all of them were attributed to the same leader. Since his death in 1923, they have not been repeated, and the younger men do not remember the words. In 1941 a Havasupai said, "If I should sing those songs improperly, the powers prayed to in the songs would give me a bad way. That's why I don't want to sing those songs."

Thus, for a while the trappings of the borrowed gods lived on in a new ritual, with new meanings. In the dancing in lines, the use of ribbons and old-style costumes, in the painting of the body and the drawing of fingers through the wet paint, in the use of disguise, and in the singing of four verses of alternating parts we find very clearly the old Hopi kachina dance patterns—remade, remodeled, and revised to meet the needs of a different people. But by 1941 even these made-over clothes of the gods had been discarded. Although one did not dance to the songs a dead man had dreamed, there was nothing to prevent men from dreaming new songs with the same purpose and the same techniques. The content of dreams reflected the interests and drives of the dreamers, and the trappings of the gods began to be left out of Havasupai thought—conscious and unconscious. By 1941, they were not even interested in the ways of the old gods.

AMERICANS BECOME AMERICANS

The blue waters of Cataract Creek do not keep their identity forever, but mingle with the great, red waters of the Colorado and eventually blend with the oceans of the world. So, too, in the early 1940s the stream of Havasupai life was blending. Certainly it will be a long time before the descendents of these people lose their Indian identity, but America is full of minority groups, and, like these, the Havasupai are also Americans. They are distinctive in some ways, but, fundamentally, they are part of a larger society which imposes upon its citizens privileges and responsibilities, not only for themselves, but for their local communities, for their country, and for the world as a whole.

In 1941, most of the younger Havasupai were using their rights to life, liberty, and the pursuit of happiness in a typical American fashion: working on the railroad, earning money as cowboys, janitors, school teachers, and farmers. They could be seen going to the rodeos, to the movies, buying and selling cattle, and window shopping. With these rights also came responsibilities—service in the army, voting, developing a knowledge of the world, and helping develop its future. Such responsibilities did not come without training or experience. At first the Havasupai had neither the knowledge nor the training to assume responsibility within the nation, so the government appointed agents and subagents to administer their rights and responsibilities for them. As a group they needed help and training, a type of training which comes through sharing responsibilities.

The training necessary to adapt Havasupai society to the mainstream of American life involved disruption of traditional culture in many fields, including medicine, community administration, and political responsibilities. In 1941 there were particular difficulties in the field of medicine. In general, shamans had not gained in stature under white contact, since their specific social functions came into conflict with those of the resident nurse and government doctors. While by 1941 there had been no wholesale acceptance of the government-sponsored curing techniques, the position of the shamans had been held up to ridicule and their general status had been weakened. Ambitious youngsters no longer respected the shaman's position or considered it a means of social advancement. The position of shaman was occupied by those who were inclined to be ultra-conservative or by those who opposed the government. As a result, the quality of the shamans was deteriorating, and the Havasupai were caught between two cultures.

Administrative responsibilities within the tribe had formerly centered on the chiefs. The position of the chiefs varied considerably over the years, but the gradual restriction of the range of the group and the eventual establishment of a permanent village within the valley tended to increase their power and prestige. In the early 1940s the attitude of the U.S. government was that chiefs were the responsible political officers of the group, but in reality most of the responsibilities of chieftainship had been taken over by the government. For example, the control of the relatively elaborate irrigation system was a responsibility of the resident sub-agent. The chiefs no longer called for volunteer labor for communal projects, such as in the maintenance of the trails; the men who did this work were paid out of government appropriations. The chiefs no longer set the calendar or gave advice about the planting seasons. The standards for moral behavior were to a great extent set by white officials, and the deviations permitted were demonstrated by white visitors, the newspapers, and other contacts with Euro-American culture. Responsibility for enforcement of the law had been taken over by white officials who were not members of the tribe. Care of old or indigent people and education of the young, which were once concerns of the chiefs, were now largely functions of the resident sub-agent or other members of the Indian Service. As the result of these developments, the position of the chief had become very much weakened and no longer carried the respect of the tribe, nor did it offer opportunities to younger men.

In 1941 an attempt was being made to organize a local tribal council. At first, this council brought together a set of younger men who, on the surface, behaved as did the old chiefs. They did a lot of talking, but the group as a whole did not like what they were saying. At the beginning it was quite evident that neither the tribe nor the members of the council themselves had any clear understanding of the delegation of elected authority which is basic to a democratic government. The new council was far from perfect, but it did represent the group, and its members tried to be responsive to the needs and wishes of those who had elected them. Thus, in the early 1940s the tribe was learning the hard way, the only way, to adapt their traditional culture to a changing world.

PART II

Havasupai Knowledge of the Natural World

The second part of this book is made up of Whiting's ethnographical information on Havasupai culture, grouped into four subject areas: weather and astronomy; minerals, metals, and rocks; animals; and plants. In the following chapters each term is defined, written phonetically, and its usage or Havasupai knowledge of it described. The information presented is based on the informants' knowledge of the item in question.

Within their categories, the lists on weather and astronomy (Chapter 11) and on minerals, metals, and rocks (Chapter 12) are presented alphabetically (except for the section on fixed stars, which is arranged in calendar order). Lists of animals (Chapter 13) and plants (Chapter 14) are grouped into their respective taxonomic sequences and are arranged alphabetically within their categories. Some final identifications are at the class or order level, while others are at the family, genus, or species levels. The last taxonomic category of the identified plant or animal depend upon Havasupai identification and usage. At times the Havasupai differentiated between the species of some plants and animals, while at other times they grouped everything into one larger category with a single term.

As in Part I, an asterisk has been used before the scientific name of a plant or animal to indicate an introduced or domesticated species. An asterisk in front of a Havasupai term indicates that it is either a reconstructed form or a portion of a longer form.

11. Weather and Astronomy

The information in this chapter was obtained with the aid of Dr. C. O. Lampland and Mr. Henry Giclas, who were both on the staff of the Lowell Observatory in 1941. Since the time the data presented here were collected, Spier (1955) has provided an extensive discussion on comparative native astronomy and calendar concepts,* and the reader is directed to his work for further information.

WEATHER AND DIRECTION CONCEPTS

Weather patterns in the area inhabited by the Havasupai often include violent storms. It is not surprising, therefore, that their weather terminology incorporated specific terms for these conditions (Table 11.1). Direction concepts (Table 11.2) referred to vague, indefinite spaces. The presence of the root -vi- in most of the direction terms clearly indicates the nature of these concepts. They were not directions from a given point, nor were they used in "giving directions." Such instructions were given in terms of known geographic features, not in terms of "north," "south," "east," or "west."

The term for south apparently originally meant "downriver." Along the Colorado River, where the Yuma and Mohave live, this

---

* Whiting agreed with Spier, who felt that ethnographers were not sufficiently well acquainted with the stars to make adequate recordings of native observations. More data are needed about weather and astronomy than those presented by Spier in 1955 or in this chapter.

TABLE 11.1
Weather Concepts

Havasupai Term	English Translation
'akwii'i'	cloud
'akwii'ka	a cloudy sky, "having clouds"
'akwiimacika	rain, "cloud falling in pieces"
vuu'u	to thunder
vuu'uk	thunder (noun), "that which thunders"
matahaiya	wind (noun)
vitha'a	fog, mist; "air-white"
vitaca	lightning
vitavika	lightning
hanapac	snow
paka'acimacika	to be snowing, "snow falling"
thapaka	ice
athapaci	hail, "ice fragments"
'inyacpaka	sunshine, "sun fragments"

would also have been "south." When the Maricopa, who formerly lived in this same situation, moved to the Gila, which flows west, they retained the original meaning of the term. The Havasupai seem to have lost this meaning, for here "downriver" would be north or west. This strong indication of a former residence upon the Colorado River is of great significance.

THE SUN AND THE MOON

The Sun   *"Sun"*   *'Inyaa'a'*

Sun was once a man. The Abert's squirrel, '*imuqwethita*', however, was smarter than Sun. In the course of their adventures, Sun deviated from his usual path, burning nearly everything on the surface of the earth.

The Moon   *"Moon"*   *Halaa'a*

The moon was said to be a disk chipped out of ice. Some said it was the face of a woman. Others said that the markings on the surface were a man (or a woman?), *hala'aapa'* "man in the moon," sitting under a cottonwood tree. A myth concerning the moon was recorded by Spier (1928).

TABLE 11.2
Direction Concepts

Havasupai Term	English Translation
vi'i	region, space (literally, "air")
*vi-ka	space, a region without a specific location (literally, "that which has air")
mata'-vika	north
kawe-vika	south (cf. Maricopa *kave* "down-river" or "west")
nya-ca'a'lo've	east (literally "place where the sun is trying to be" or "sun-rising place")
nya-to'po-vi	west (literally, "sun-setting place")
imiyaa	sky (literally, "above")

MOVING STARS AND PLANETS

Evening Star   "Large Star"   *Hamasi'kuvete'e'*

At various times several planets were called by this name; they were all considered to be one star.

Morning Star   "Lazy Star"   *Hamasi'kithulva*

At various times different planets played this role. The morning star was considered lazy because the other stars had been shining all night, but this one shone for just a short while early in the morning.

THE FIXED STARS

Star   "Star"   *Hamasi'i'*

The Havasupai distinguished between the fixed stars and the more obvious moving stars, or planets. They recognized several star clusters, many of which were important in determining the calendar (see Chapter 9; Table 9.2). Knowledge of the stars appeared to be general throughout the group and was not the specialized knowledge of the chiefs, as was the sun calendar. Many stars played a part in mythology, and, undoubtedly, every child knew the personalities associated with the more important stars. In 1941 there was no indication that these mythical personalities were still active, for there was no personification of the stars in daily life. They were not addressed

specifically in prayers, although they were sometimes included in the
totality of nature which the Havasupai addressed from time to time.

Certain stars were important in judging time, not only within the
year, but also within the period of a single night.

Milky Way — — — *Yemtava*

No translation was obtained for this term. The Walapai equivalents,
icil-camnyunaca "(women) traveling to get shells" and *thava-nyuunyace* "dust trail" are suggestive, but not conclusive, cognate
materials (Spier 1955).

STAR CLUSTERS

The following information on Havasupai knowledge of constellations
is arranged in seasonal order, beginning with spring, through summer, fall, and winter. The last star cluster described, *helopaavaca*,
was visible during the entire year.

Hyades "Wives of the Bat" *Heca'a'*

Visible from July until May. General descriptions and diagrams showing the position of this constellation relative to Orion make identification absolutely certain. The Walapai and the Maricopa also recognized
a similar group by this name (usually identified in the literature as the
Pleiades).

This was one of the few star clusters which the Havasupai did not
apparently mention in their mythology. They stated that the Walapai
and the Yavapai had stories about these stars, but that they themselves did not. The appearance of these stars, said by S.J. to be the
wives of the bat, marked the month *kavotasapeka* (ca. July).

Orion "Bighorn Sheep" *Amu'u'*

Visible from mid-July or early August until May. The association of
bighorn sheep with the constellation Orion was widespread in this
area. The three stars of the belt were variously identified as a flock of
bighorn sheep (*amu'u'*) or as an antelope, a deer, and a bighorn
sheep. They were being ambushed by the star Rigel, who was known
as Wolf Man (*hatakwila*). Orion's sword was identified as an arrow.
The sheep were being chased into the ambush by Coyote Man
(Betelgeuse). The appearance of this star cluster marked the month
kavo-pawaca (August).

The Tail of Leo   "Hand"   *Sal*

First visible in August, these stars were described as a circular group, with one star in the palm and one for each finger. There seem to be three possible identifications: Corona, Auriga, and the tail of Leo. This star cluster marked the month *sal-ciola*, which immediately follows August. The terms for this group of stars were loosely applied, and there was a distinct implication that this group appeared about September. This time of appearance would eliminate Auriga as a possibility, since it rises before, not after, Orion, the marker of the preceding month. Corona rises in November, which would be too late, if the Havasupai month sequence has any validity. Furthermore, there seems to be another name for Corona. The tail of the constellation Leo appears at the right time and matches the description of the cluster. Similar information comes from the Walapai (Kroeber 1935).

This star cluster was considered to be a very important group, as it marked the beginning of the year for the Havasupai. There was a general tendency to suggest that it appeared in November, which may be, in part, its confusion with Corona. It may also have been linked with the difficulties of adjusting the lunar cycle to the solar year. This was the period, at the end of one year and the beginning of another, when a disharmony in the lunar and solar cycles would have had to be adjusted. Such an adjustment would have been necessary about once every three years.

Corona Borealis   "Hoop"   *Tavacuta*

Although this constellation appears in November, is was not associated with the Havasupai calendar month for November, *hala'apa'kinueeva*. It was named after the hoop of the hoop-and-pole game.

Spica, Arcturus, Denebola (?)   "The Horn"   *Muqwawa*

"The Horn" was said to consist of three bright stars at a considerable distance from each other. It was not considered to be an important group, and little information could be obtained other than that it preceded *'ipe'e'* (Scorpio). Eliminating stars which are known to have been part of some other Havasupai cluster, and searching the sky to the west of Scorpio, we find Spica and Arcturus and, perhaps, Denebola as possible candidates.

Scorpio   "Carrying Pole"   *Ipe'e'*

This winter constellation appears first in December and is visible into July. There is a legend about *'ipe'e'*: Mountain Lion Man came into Coyote Man's camp one night. Coyote wanted the other man's girl, but Mountain Lion sent him out for firewood. Coyote returned with a long pole which was considered too valuable to burn, so Mountain Lion told him to go out again to the west and come back from the east. Every time Coyote and his pole came by, he wanted to stop, but Mountain Lion kept telling him to keep on going. Coyote is now a star carrying a pole (a row of lesser stars) across the sky.

The appearance of this constellation marked the month *'ipe'ca'akia* (December?). It was known among the Walapai as *hine*, the name of the long pole used to gather giant cactus (saguaro) fruit (Kroeber 1935).

The Havasupai, who were not acquainted with the giant saguaro cactus, and who did not use a fruit-gathering pole, had apparently changed the name to something comprehensible in their culture, but had failed to explain why the pole was of such value to Coyote that he was still, after all these years, reluctant to burn it.

Altair, Aquila   "Cold Star"   *Hamasi'katati'a*

These stars, which set soon after sunset, first appear in January. Altair was called *hate'u'u'*. Associated with *hate'u'u'* were three other stars (the constellation Aquila), which represented his two wives and a baby. *Hate'u'u'* was stolen from his people and after many adventures returned to join his two wives and child. In retaliation for past treatment he killed all of the tribe except his family. He demanded food, and his wives fed him on the flesh of the people he had killed. After he had gorged himself, he asked to be assisted to the edge of the cliff where he could relieve himself. He fell over the edge, pulling his family with him. They were all killed and became the star cluster *hamasi'katati'a*. This star cluster's appearance marked the month *mamasi'katati'a*—roughly, February. Among the Walapai it was known as *celqa-loya* "interrupted defecation" (Kroeber 1935). In the Havasupai name, *katati'a* means "cold."

Ursa Major (The Big Dipper)   "Turning Stars"   *Hamasi'sikuwaiiva*

Native drawings and field identifications indicate that this constellation was Ursa Major. This identification is also consistent with the statement that it "follows *amu'u'* (Orion) and *heca'a'* (Hyades)." Although it was visible throughout the year, it was most prominent in the spring. People versed in the knowledge of the stars could tell the time of night by its position in the sky.

— — —   **"Baking Cottontails"**   *Helopaavaca*

This group had three stars in a row and was visible all year round. Walapai data suggest a faint cluster with a large star on each side (Kroeber 1935). This was possibly Ursa Minor (the Little Dipper) of Cassiopeia. For the Havasupai it represented two men who were cooking cottontail rabbits in an earth oven (in the name, *helo* refers to cottontail and *paava* to bake). The Havasupai did not consider this star cluster important.

12. Minerals, Metals, and Rocks

The Havasupai were familiar with a number of minerals, metals, and rocks in their region. These items were incorporated into their culture in various ways, including use in paints and dyes, tools, hunting equipment, pottery, and jewelry.

Chert   **"Leathery Rock"**   *Awi-qlisa'a*

Descriptions of the use of this rock indicate a chert. Pieces were struck with a flint knife to produce a spark for the strike-a-light, the Havasupai equivalent to flint and steel.

The name can be translated (*awi-* rock, *qlisa* leathery) leathery rock, referring to the surface texture. Spier (1928) gave a term which would be written as *ota-kiskwia*, (*ota-* fire-producing; *kis-*, possibly *qlisa*, leathery; *kwi* to twist or strike), "the fire-producing leathery thing which is struck."

Clay   **Pottery Clay**   *Amatkaiya*

The best pottery clay, which was the color of adobe, was obtained in Walapai country near Pine Springs. Another deposit near Hermit's Rest on the south rim of the Grand Canyon was also used. Such clay was hard, and chunks had to be pried loose with a deer-antler pick (Spier 1928).

Copper Carbonates   **Green Paint**   — — —

These minerals were available near Grandview on the south rim of the Grand Canyon. The Havasupai used them to decorate buckskin clothing (Spier 1928). They were also traded with the Hopi.

Flint — — — *Akwa'a*

Flint knives and arrowpoints were made. The stone was flaked on the heel of the hand with an antler-tip cylinder (Spier 1928). Flint, often in the form of a knife, was used in the native strike-a-light. Drilling in wood, bone, or horn was done with flint arrowpoints by revolving the arrow shaft between the hands (Spier 1928). The name that used to apply to flint knives and points later referred to metal knives and points.

Gypsum **White Paint** *Matahe'e*

This white, gravel-like mineral was found near the village and near the head of Lee Canyon. It was roasted in ashes for several hours, then ground to a powder, put in a pan, and stirred with a little water until it thickened. In this form it was used to paint the body when a hunter wished to disguise himself as an antelope. It was used as a face paint during some of the dances, and it was used on horses during the Horse Song in a similar manner. In the name, *mat* refers to "earth" and *hai* to "white." The name for white man was *hai'iku'u* (*hai-* white, - *hu'u* head), "he who has a white head." It must be remembered that the Indians were called redskins because they painted their skins red. The Havasupai apparently returned the compliment by calling Anglos "those who look like they are painted white," with the implication that the difference was less than skin deep.

Halite **Table Salt** *'Ithii'i*

The Havasupai formerly obtained salt from several sources. The deposits within Cataract Canyon near the village yielded an inferior grade, which was red. These deposits were readily accessible, and the salt was simply broken off and taken home. The supply of relatively pure salt in the Grand Canyon could be reached only with difficulty. One left the rim and descended by a foot trail to a point near the Colorado River. From here a man was let down over a low cliff by means of a rope made of braided strands of bighorn sheep hide. Here the salt hung "like icicles" from the roof of a big cave. Pieces of this rock-like deposit were broken off and placed in sacks in amounts weighing from twenty-five to thirty pounds. Before leaving the cave, the collector—or the oldest person present, if there were several—addressed the salt, telling of the trials of the journey out of the canyon and asking for help for them all. If this prayer was not spoken, it was thought that the men would get tired and develop cramps in their legs and not be able to get out of the canyon. The cave deposit was called *ithii'ya* ('*ithi'i* salt, *ya-* to contain). Along the Little Colorado River there were several salt deposits; the river was, therefore, called *ahaka-thiela* (*ahaka-* river, '*ithi'i-* salt, *- l-* to turn into) "salty river."

The red salt, with marked impurities, was placed in a vessel of water, and the dissolved salt was then poured off to be used in cooking, leaving the impurities behind. In contrast, the white salt was ground up for use directly on food, as during a meal. The Havasupai, like the Hopi and other Indian groups in the area, used only small quantities of salt while cooking; this is one of the reasons that Indian food has frequently been characterized as flat and tasteless.

Salt was not fed to infants, for it was thought that it would cause white sores on the tongue (Spier 1928). Similarly, a new mother must avoid salt, for it would dry up the flow of milk, just as salt on the ground makes the ground hard (Spier 1928). Mescal would be bitter if the people baking it ate salt during the process. Bee stings were squeezed and salt rubbed on the swollen area (Spier 1928).

Hematite, Red Ochre   Red Paint   *Akwata*

The name *ka-hwata* simply means "something red." The locations of hematite deposits were supposed to be secret; some of these have long been known as the "lost Mines of the Padres." Spier (1928) placed the major mines on Diamond Creek in what is now the Walapai Reservation. Kroeber (1935) placed them on Diamond Creek and in Meriwitica Canyon. Additional deposits were known to occur east of Cataract Canyon in the Grand Canyon area. Deposits on the north side of the Colorado River were worked by the Paiute around 1875 (Dellenbaugh 1934). The Hopi were ignorant of any of these deposits and relied completely upon trade with the Havasupai and Walapai for their supply. Through the Hopi, the red paint passed east to many other tribes, particularly the Pueblo peoples of New Mexico. The Walapai apparently supplied the Yuman tribes along the Colorado, including the Halchichoma and the Maricopa (Spier 1933).

The best-known deposit in the Walapai country, which was exploited by both Havasupai and Walapai, was in a small cave high on the face of a cliff. It was a difficult and dangerous procedure to mine this cave deposit, which was reached by a ladder (made by tying several poles together). Only one man could enter at a time, so one man usually collected for the entire group. He crawled into the cave on his stomach, pried the material loose from the deposit with a stick (in 1941, with a crowbar), and worked it into a sack held under his arm. This cave deposit was not worked as much in recent times, as it was formerly. Many of the Walapai were content to pick up old pieces of ore which had fallen from the mine, and other deposits were also available to the Havasupai farther east in the Grand Canyon.

When the men went on an expedition to a difficult mine, they insisted that a prayer be said before they removed the material from the canyon. If this was not done, the material became excessively heavy, the weight increasing as one neared the rim of the canyon. If a person had been particularly disrespectful, he might not be able to climb back up to the rim at all: "Sometimes men die." The prayers asked that the pain remain light for the men's travels out of the canyon.

There were a number of methods for preparing hematite paint. One method was to toast the fresh material in a metal container (this task was performed only by women). The red color would darken over the fire. The mineral was removed, allowed to cool, and ground. Some used a special grinding stone two and a half feet long and one foot wide; others used a regular grinding stone but washed it off carefully after the paint was made. A tank northwest of Drift Fence was called *akwatatahulca* because hematite was often ground there.

The roasted, ground ore, which was dry and powdery, might be mixed with water and molded into a cake, in which form it was traded. A small amount of the molded paint base was kept in a leather bag. When paint was needed, material was scraped from the cake with a fingernail and combined with a little freshly chewed deer grease in the palm of the hand. Once the base had been mixed with the deer grease, the paint would not keep for more than a month or two. Cushing (1882) stated that oil extracted from sunflower seeds might be used instead of deer grease, but this was not confirmed in 1941. The Hopi applied the dry paint directly to the face without adding grease.

The Havasupai applied face paint with the fingers, using a variety of patterns, which Spier (1928) described in detail. Before long dresses were worn, a woman's legs were also often painted. By 1941 the elaborately detailed face paintings were rarely seen, but a liberal coating of red paint was frequently applied to other parts of the body as a protection against sunburn. In general, women painted regularly, men only upon special occasions.

The soothing paint might also be applied to the chapped hands of a small child, or the dry paint dusted on the bodies of infants to prevent chafing (Spier 1928). Red paint was often applied by the Havasupai to a variety of leather goods, such as the ball used in playing shinny (Spier 1928), and buckskin clothing of various kinds. Used in this manner, the paint was probably not very satisfactory, but, because there was a limited supply of good vegetable dye, it was used rather commonly. It was often added to mescal paint to thicken it (Spier 1928) and was also put on the outside of water bottles and basketry cups before the final layer of pinyon pitch was applied to these items.

This red paint was perhaps the most important thing the Havasupai had to offer in trade to other native groups. The standard price among the Hopi and the New Mexico Pueblo tribes in 1941 was twenty-five cents a teaspoonful (measures were fairly generous, however). Larger amounts were traded for high prices in goods or cash (Table 12.1).

Iron Pyrites   Fool's Gold   *O'oota*

Iron pyrites were known to occur at the Bass Mine and in many other locations in the Grand Canyon area. Gold and fool's gold had the same name.

Metal   — — —   *Akwa'a*

There was no use of native metals in early times. By 1880 commercial iron knives were replacing flint and obsidian (Cushing 1882), and the change was complete by 1910 (Spier 1918). In 1881 Cushing observed no stone-tipped arrows, only wood or metal, but bits of wire were being used for awls and needles (Cushing 1882). By the early 1800s brass kettles were competing with earthen pots, and at this time Cushing mentioned earrings and bangles made of silver or brass. In the early 1900s Curtis (1908) photographed a man wearing metal earrings.

The Havasupai had several terms for metals: gold was called *o'oota* (see discussion under iron pyrites); silver—and metal coins—

TABLE 12.1
Trade Value of Red Ochre Paint in 1941

Amount of Paint	Exchange Value
1 teaspoon	for a ring, or 25¢ cash
5 teaspoons	for a bracelet
1 pound	for a blanket
5 pounds	for a concho belt
1 cigar box, "not too full"	for a saddle blanket
1 baking-powder can, full	for $10 cash
1-lb. coffee can, half full	for $2 cash
4-lb. lard can, full	for a blanket, sash, and some bracelets

generally were called *umpaa'isa*; the term for iron (or for metal in general) derives from the old word for flint, *akwaa'a*.

Stone knives and arrowheads were called *kwayal*, and knives made of horn were called simply *aqwaa'a*. Apparently the first metals obtained by the Havasupai were metal knives, and so the old terms for horn and knife were extended to include metals generally. As new uses of metal were introduced, new names were derived from older terms. For example, a fork was called *kwak-sapa* "a knife with points," and a metal spoon became *qwam-kwa'a* "metal spoon." Copper was described as *akwa'a-kwatha* "yellow metal," and a man with gold teeth was identified as *kwa-yai-ya* "he who has metal teeth."

Obsidian   **Volcanic Glass**   *Kwayaca*

Black or, sometimes, a clear obsidian was used for arrowpoints and for knives. In a myth, Duck was sent under water to get some black obsidian. The obsidian he obtained was broken up, so that there were a great many sharp edges, and placed in the abdominal cavity of an orphan, who was then fed to a man-eating giant bird. As the body of the orphan was being digested, the obsidian cut up the interior of the giant bird, and he died; with his death, numerous captives were liberated.

Sphalerite-Galena   **Zinc and Lead Ore**   *Amatinyaac*

This material was scraped from a stratum in a trench at Pine Springs on the Walapai reservation, and the powder was kept in a buckskin bag to make a black paint. To make the paint, a stick moistened in the mouth was inserted in the nearly closed neck of the bag. The resulting mixture was painted on the face for war parties or used to attract a girl. Grease was not used in making this paint. At one time this material was traded as far east as the Zuni (Bunzel 1932), but by 1941 the trench deposit had been covered up and was no longer in use.

Unknown Mineral   **Blue Paint**   *Matahavasuua'*

This mineral, which was no longer used in 1941, came from a deposit in the Grand Canyon. Formerly it was used in face painting by both men and women, particularly for dances.

13. The Animal Kingdom

Information reported in this chapter was obtained with the aid of collections from Grand Canyon Natural History Association (later Grand Canyon National Park) and the Museum of Northern Arizona. While some data were gathered by observation of animals in their natural habitat, none of the physical information pertaining to birds was obtained by direct observation of living birds. The descriptions, identifications, habits, songs, ranges, and ethnographic significance of birds were prepared with the help of Allan Phillips (then Curator of Ornithology at the Museum of Northern Arizona). Mr. Phillips also assisted in the field work and in the original drafting of the bird section of this manuscript.

According to Havasupai mythology, a number of animals were also men (Table 13.1). Like the animals in the stories of Chicken Little and Mickey Mouse, these animal-men had the power of speech and the motivations and desires of men, but they also retained their animal properties, so they were capable of acting like both men and animals. It is also apparent that there were a number of animals who "never were men" and who always appeared in the myths exactly as

Over the years many changes have occurred in the taxonomic classification of animals. Since the time of Whiting's work with the Havasupai, many of the animals' scientific names, as well as their taxonomic classification, have been changed. The scientific terminology and taxonomic sequence used in this chapter reflect the data recognized in 1984 and, therefore, differ somewhat from Whiting's original work.

TABLE 13.1
Animals Who Were Men in Havasupai Myths

Scientific Name	English Common Name
Aquila chrysaetos	Eagle
Calliphoridae	Fly
Canis latrans	Coyote
Canis lupus	Wolf
Cervus canadensis	Elk
Colaptes auratus	Flicker
Crotalidae	Snake (Rattlesnake)
Erethizon dorsatum	Porcupine
Felis concolor	Mountain Lion
Formicidae	Ant
Hemipterae	Bug
Leporidae	Rabbit
Meleagris gallopavo	Turkey
Muscicapidae	Bluebird
Peromyscus manicalatus	Mouse
Rodentia	Rodent
Sauromalus obesus	Chuckwalla
Sciurus aberti	Squirrel
Scorpionidae	Scorpion
Strigidae	Owl
Troglodytidae	Wren
Urocyon cinereoargenteus	Fox
Vespertilionidae	Bat

TABLE 13.2
Animals Who Were Never Men in Havasupai Myths

Scientific Name	English Common Name
Bos taurus	Cow
Canis familiaris	Dog
Colubridae	Snake (other than rattlesnake)
Equus caballus	Horse
Felis sylvestris	Cat
Lepidoptera	Butterfly
Odocoileus hemionus	Deer
Ursus americanus	Bear

*Introduced species

they actually appeared in real life (Table 13.2). The idea was expressed by one informant (P.B.) that if an animal appeared in one myth as an animal, he would never appear in any myth as a man. Other myths tell how humans became animals, such as bighorn sheep and buffaloes.

PHYLUM MOLLUSCA

CLASS GASTROPODA

Order Archaeogastropoda

FAMILY HALIOTIDAE

Species Not Differentiated   Abalone (Shell)   *Halakidapa*

Abalone shell was obtained from either the Hopi or Walapai. The Walapai obtained it from the Mohave who, in turn, had trade connections with people who lived near the ocean. Abalone was formerly used in shell pendants. By 1941 it was a well-known form of medicine for barren women. A piece of shell about half an inch square was pounded and ground into a fine powder, mixed with water, and administered to the patient as a drink.

In a myth, Wolf Man stirred pieces of abalone shell in a water hole to produce a baby. When this baby grew up he turned into a bighorn sheep who, after a series of adventures, became Orion.

The name for abalone shell breaks down to the following: *ha-*water, *la-* to be in, *kidapa-* butterfly or iridescence.

PHYLUM ARTHROPODA

CLASS CHILOPODA

Order Not Differentiated   Centipedes   *Hanyiqlisava*

The Havasupai considered a centipede bite to be fatal. Sometimes a person's life could be saved if the wound was cut and sucked, preferably by a doctor. It was a common belief that, if a person was bitten by one of these creatures, he would get well if he counted the number of the animal's legs correctly. The centipede was one of the ingredients in arrow poison.

CLASS ARACHNIDA

Order Scorpionida

| *Families Not Differentiated* | Scorpions | *Niisa* |

A large form, *niisata*, was said to be particularly dangerous. P.B. made a drawing showing a black area in the back of the animal, where "it carries its poison. It goes down the tail and causes the sting." This dark patch was removed and the contents rubbed on arrow points intended for use against human enemies. Even a slight wound made the victim sicken and die in two weeks. Spier (1928) listed this black substance as one of the ingredients of arrow poison. He also stated that "Scorpion stings are treated similarly to snake bites and possibly by the snake doctor alone. Incisions are made about the ligated wound and the blood sucked out."

Order Araneida

FAMILY THERIDIIDAE

| *Latrodectus mactans* | Black Widow | *Amatkenyuwei'i* |

Apparently all spiders went by this name, but, strictly speaking, the Havasupai term refers to a poisonous form, presumably the black widow. The bite was said to have serious results, and a medicine man might be called to sing for a person who had been bitten. This spider was listed as one of the ingredients of arrow poison (Spier 1928). The Havasupai name for spider was derived from the following: *amat*-earth *kinyuwei'i* (*ka*- who has, *-nya*- his, *-wa*- house) "he who lived in the ground." The web was called *amatkenyume'e*.

| *Eurypelma* spp. | Tarantula | *Aqwakavace* |

Large, hairy spiders found near Grand Canyon Village.

CLASS INSECTA

Order Odonata

FAMILY LIBELLULIDAE

| *Libellula quadrimaculata* | Dragonfly | *Cithkwilakaaheka'* |

Recognized and named, but no further data available.

Order Orthoptera

FAMILY ACRIDIDAE

Species Not Differentiated   Locusts and Grasshoppers   *Kumpammka*

The larger members of this group were called *kumpammka'tova.*

FAMILY GRYLLIDAE

Species Not Differentiated   Crickets   *Hamanyukivaso'o*

They lived in the brush and in the houses and, as the Havasupai said, they "call at night." Cushing (1882) stated that they were cooked in the parching trays and eaten.

Stenopelmatus fuscus   Jerusalem Cricket   *Hamanyukivaso'o*

The Havasupai believed that this insect might bite a baby and kill it by sucking its blood. This belief is similar to ideas held about this insect throughout the world. In the name, *hamaanya* refers to "child" and *kivaso'o* means "to take care of."

Order Anoplura

FAMILY PEDICULIDAE

Species Not Differentiated   Lice   *He'il*

Although lice were abundant on the heads of children and old people, young people were usually careful in this respect. "Lice are not eaten, just chewed and spit out." A man might shake his clothes over the fire or boil them to get rid of lice. A particularly vicious variety of lice was called *tetkoopuka;* lice "eggs" were called *hicile,* from **he-c-il,* indicating "many little things."

Order Homoptera

FAMILY CICADIDAE

Species Not Differentiated   Cicadas   *Haiyiwaa'a*

Recognized and named, but no further data available.

Order Hemiptera

FAMILY CIMICIDAE

Species Not Differentiated   Bed Bugs   *Pakicaava*

Recognized and named, but no further data available.

FAMILIES COREIDAE AND PENTATOMIDAE

Species Not Differentiated Squash Bugs and Stink Bugs *Hmteekitepuuya*

Squash and stink bugs attack squash and pumpkin vines, killing the leaves. The Havasupai name, which is the same for both families listed, breaks down to *hmtee* squash or pumpkin and *kitepuuya* poison.

Order Coleoptera

FAMILY CICINDELIDAE

Species Not Differentiated   Leaf or Tiger Beetles   *Suwakecikwina*

Beetles that were small, relatively round, and hard shelled were all classed as "little round bug." The name for beetles came from the following: *suwa* basketry water bottle, *-ci* plural (marker), *kwi* twisted; the term, thus translated "the twisted strands used to plug the mouth of the water bottle." This name makes very little sense if one looks only at the modern technique of stopping bottles with a casual twist of grass or similar fibers. However, an examination of the archaeological and historical records reveal that the narrow-mouthed jars used for the storage of seeds and similar materials were often sealed with a mass of fiber topped with a plug of clay. At other times small stones were sealed in the mouths of such vessels with lac. The appearance of such stoppers closely resembled the small, round bugs with hard wing covers which the Havasupai placed in this category.

FAMILY CARABIDAE

Calosoma spp.   Carnivorous Ground Beetles   *Cikananika*

Recognized and named, but no further data available.

FAMILY TENEBRIONIDAE

Eleodes longicollis   **Darkling Ground Beetle**   *Cikananikathite*

The name means "the *cikananika* (*Calosoma* spp.) that stinks."

FAMILY LUCANIDAE

Pseudolucanus mazama   **Cottonwood Stag Beetle**   *Cikanamikaqwava*

The name means "the *cikananika* (*Calosoma* spp.) with horns."

FAMILY SCARABAEIDAE

Species Not Differentiated   **June or Scarab Beetles**   *Thuqthmoe*

Recognized and named, but not further data available.

Order Diptera

FAMILY CALLIPHORIDAE

Species Not Differentiated   **Blow Flies**   *Thumpuutika*

"They are around dog or horse leavings, then come around my supper and that's no good!" Fly features as one of the quasi-human characters in a myth. The name comes from *thumpoo'o* bee.

FAMILY CULICIDAE

Species Not Differentiated   **Mosquitoes**   *Huuvaka*

The name means "a sharp pointed head."

Order Lepidoptera: Sub-order Heterocera

Families Not Differentiated   **Moths**   *Ool'kuvwa'a'*

Recognized and named, but no further data available.

Order Lepidoptera: Sub-order Rhopalocera

Families Not Differentiated   **Butterflies**   *Kidapa*

Recognized and named, but no further data available.

Order Hymenoptera

FAMILY APIDAE

| *Species Not Differentiated* | **Bees** | *Thumpoo'o* |

Bees were found in old, dead trees, in hollow stumps, or in such places as the dead flower stalks of mescal. Parties of children went out to gather such stalks, then split them open, and collected the honey (Spier 1928). E.U. talked of building a fire to smoke the bees out of a hollow tree. P.B. said that one should cover the face with a sack and wear gloves. Bee stings were squeezed and then salt was rubbed onto them (Spier 1928).

FAMILY POMPILIDAE

| *Species Not Differentiated* | **Spider Wasps** | *Na'iketu'u* |

The sting of these insects was said to burn, but there was no treatment for it.

FAMILY FORMICIDAE

| *Species Not Differentiated* | **Black Ants** | *Cinapuka* |
| *Pogonomyrmex* spp. | **Harvester Ants** | *Cimmi'yul* |

The species *P. barbatus* was known to bite and sting severely (Essig 1926). The sting of these red ants was said to hurt and to cause swelling. This swelling might be avoided if a folder leaf of Jimson weed (*Datura meteloides*) was rubbed over the spot. These ants were said to make anthills, *cimmi'yul-nyiwa'a* "red ant, his house." The tiny, little stones from such hills might be taken home "to clean bottles," or be used for temper for pottery clay (Spier 1928). This ant was also one of the ingredients in arrow poison.

In one myth, Ant took the other quasi-human creatures down into his hole in order to avoid Sun's wrath. In another myth, Fox sent Fly out to bite the mouth of a supposedly dead giant. The failure of the giant to react was considered evidence that he might be dead. Fox, however, did not think this evidence was adequate and sent Ant to bite him on the mouth and eyes. Still Fox was not satisfied and he sent Scorpion to bite him. Finally Fox went to investigate for himself. This myth reflects the Havasupai attitude toward the severity of these bites—i.e., an ant bite was worse than a fly bite, but not as bad as a scorpion.

PHYLUM CHORDATA: SUB-PHYLUM VERTEBRATA

CLASS OSTEICHTHYES

Orders Not Differentiated   Fishes   *Icii'i'*

Fish are not native to Cataract Creek. Cataract Creek has been stocked several times, but flood waters often take the fish out. The Havasupai knew that there were fish in the Colorado River, but, for the most part, they did not eat fish, although some people who worked away from the village had learned to eat them.

CLASS AMPHIBIA

Order Caudata

FAMILY AMBYSTOMIDAE

Ambystoma tigrinum   Tiger Salamander   *Hanyakalaapa'*

They were found in tanks on the Plateau, where water was found the year around. Describing his trip to Havasupai Canyon in 1881, Coues (1900) wrote, "Black tank was a nasty hole in the rocks, containing perhaps 5,000 gallons of dead water and filth in which lurked an enormous number of repulsive fishes with legs or axolotls, also called guaholotes—a species of *Amblystoma*."

B.B. expressed the fear that one of these creatures would crawl into bed with him and he would wake to find it asleep in his armpit or crotch. Not exactly a pleasant thought from the standpoint of either party. The name breaks down from the following words: *hanya'a'* frog and *ka-laapa'* flat.

Order Anura

Families Not Differentiated   Frogs and Toads   *Hanya'a'*

Adult frogs and toads, as well as their tadpoles (called *ha'ila'*) were abundant in the river and irrigation ditches in the village. They were apparently not used for food, because "pulling a frog to pieces causes a flood" (Spier 1928). A notched stick, laid flat on an inverted coiled tray basket was rubbed with another stick. The grating noise was said to resemble a frog and to produce rain. The practice of calling for rain in this manner was thought to have been copied from the Hopi (Spier 1928). B.B. was very explicit about killing frogs. He stated that "if you kill a lot of them, they will make heavy rains. Big floods will come and wash the village away. Therefore, we don't kill frogs and we tell the children to keep away from them."

CLASS REPTILIA

Order Squamata: Sub-order Sauria

FAMILY GEKKONIDAE

Coleonyx variegatus   **Variegated Ground Geko**   *Amat'hamaanya*

The head of this harmless lizard is shaped like that of the rattlesnake. The Havasupai said, "He is mean, like a rattlesnake." They considered the bite poisonous. Rock Jones, a medicine man who had died before 1941, was said to have treated the wound by cutting it open and sucking out the "poison," as was done for rattlesnake bites. M.T. said that if you bothered it, this animal caused rain and hail in the same manner as the chuckwalla. The name means "child of the earth," from *amat* earth and *hamaanya* child.

FAMILY IGUANIDAE

Crotaphytus collaris   **Collared Lizard**   *Tuvuna'a'*

Recognized and named, but no further data available.

Phrynosoma douglasii   **Short-horned Lizard**   *Telqwam*

This was locally known as the "horned toad." The name came from the term *qwa*, meaning "horn."

Sauromalus obesus   **Chuckwalla**   *'Umthul*

These great, gray lizards lived in cracks in the rocks and were found in Cataract Canyon and on the Plateau. The Walapai used to eat chuckwalla, but they believed that disturbing the Gila monster would cause rain and destructive storms (Kroeber 1935). The origin of this Walapai belief probably rests upon the peculiar habits of the Gila monster, which, when disturbed, will attack, foaming at the mouth, drooling poison and saliva, and breathing out his habitually vile breath (Dodge 1949). The association with rain was heightened by the high decorative coloring of the fine, bead-like scales, which looked like hail on a pink background. The Havasupai, who were unfamiliar with the Gila monster, fused these two concepts and attributed the attack behavior, the "hail-looking back," and the role of the Gila monster in Walapai myths to the chuckwalla. In contrast to the Walapai, the Havasupai did not eat chuckwallas; they also avoided disturbing this animal and considered that, if not poisonous, it was dangerous because it could cause destructive storms.

In Havasupai mythology, Chuckwalla Man attempted to rescue *hate'u'u* (the star Altair) by blowing smoke from a pipe into a crack in a cliff where Altair was held prisoner. The smoke cracked the rock and Chuckwalla then climbed part way up the cliff, but he was unable to complete the rescue. In another story he caused heavy snow and hail, which resulted in the death of his enemies.

Sceloporus magister   **Desert Spiny Lizard**   *Taathila'kuvete'e'*

Recognized and named, but no further data available.

Sceloporus undulatus   **Eastern Fence Lizard**   *Taathila'*

Recognized and named, but no further data available.

FAMILY TEIIDAE

Cnemidophorus velox   **Western Spotted Racerunner**   *Katuula'*

The Havasupai name probably referred to several different species which were abundant in the vicinity of the village in Cataract Canyon.

Order Squamata: Sub-order Serpentes

FAMILY COLUBRIDAE

Hypsiglena torquata   **Spotted Night Snake**   *Hatamaala*

Although it has little or no effect on humans, the venom is fatal to small, cold-blooded animals. This fact may explain the disagreement among the Havasupai about whether or not it was poisonous.

Lampropeltis getulus   **Common King Snake**   *Hanyipuuka*

Lampropeltis pyromelana   **Mountain King Snake**   *Hanyipuuka*

These two species were probably not differentiated from each other or from the California king snake. These snakes have striking black and white markings. Informants agreed that they were not poisonous and that they were found in Cataract Canyon. P.B. thought they fought with rattlesnakes. The name translates as "long cylindrical frog," from *hanya'a* frog and *puuka* long and cylindrical. A spring in Cataract Canyon where the walls are banded like a king snake was called *hanyipuuk-niha'a* (*-ni-* down, *ha'a* water).

Masticophus bilineatus **Whipsnake** *'Iluwi'hala'llta'iita*

Thamnophis elegans **Great Basin Garter Snake** *'Iluwi'hala'llta'iita*

The Havasupai did not distinguish between these two snakes, both of which are nonpoisonous, with yellow, white, and dark bands running the length of the back. These were long snakes, found in Cataract Canyon, which could move quickly and tended to stay near the water.

Pituophis melanoleucus **Bull Snake** *'Iluwi'iita*

This large snake was thought to attack men and horses, but it was not considered poisonous by most Havasupai. The name means "elongated rattlesnake," from *'iluwi'i* rattlesnake and *'iita* long and cylindrical.

FAMILY CROTALIDAE

Crotalus spp. **Rattlesnakes** *'Iluwi'i*
   C. viridis (Western Rattlesnake)

   C. molossus (Black-tailed Rattlesnake)

Although there were a number of different forms found within this area, the Havasupai did not differentiate between them. They all had rattles (*'iluwi'kethituva*), their bite was thought to be fatal, and their disposition was known to be mean.

Rattlesnakes were killed by throwing stones at the head of the snake. If there was any chance that man's wife was pregnant, he did not kill the snake since it would cause his child to be born with weak limbs and have to crawl on the ground like a snake.

Snake bites were usually treated by special snake doctors, although, in the absence of such a specialist, others were permitted to operate. The doctor would tie the arm or leg, open the wound with a knife, and suck the wound, spitting out the blood and poison (Spier 1928). Snake doctors also had the power to control the snakes.

CLASS AVES

The name for the eagle (*asa'a*) appears to have been used also as a general term for birds, although the combination term '*icisa'a*, meaning "those who are birds," was in more general use. Similar terminology was found throughout most of the Yuman languages. The term *aciye'r*, meaning "those who fly," was found in Yuma, Maricopa, and Mohave, and the Kiliwa term *kewalo*, which translates as "having wings," was similar in idea, if not in form. Other Indian terms for "bird" are: Cocopa *shya'*, Diegueño *asa*, and Seri *siik*. The Havasupai word for birds' nests was *nopee'e*, for eggs it was *sakawa*, and for birds' eggs it was *icisa'sakawa*.

Order Podicipediformes

FAMILY PODICIPEDIDAE

Species Not Differentiated   Grebes   *Qlinamoo'kithula*

In the name, *qlinamoo'o* means "ducks" and *kithula* means "lazy."

Order Ciconiiformes

FAMILY ARDEIDAE

Species Not Differentiated   Herons   *Huu'ikiyula*

Members of this group were occasionally seen near the village. The name means "long head," from *huu'u* head and *kiyula* long.

Order Anseriformes

FAMILY ANATIDAE

Species Not Differentiated   Ducks   *Qlinamoo'o*

Ducks, often seen in Cataract Canyon, were shot with reed arrows. The feathers were pulled out and the entrails, head, and legs were removed. If several birds were available, they might be cut into pieces; if only one had been shot, it would be thrown into the pot whole and boiled for three hours. Diving ducks were called by the same name that the Havasupai used for grebes (*qlinamoo'kithula*) and were not distinguished from grebes.

Order Falconiformes

FAMILY CATHARTIDAE

Cathartes aura   Turkey Vulture   *Asa'a*

Recognized and named, but no further data available.

FAMILY ACCIPITRIDAE

Accipiter cooperii   Cooper's Hawk   *Kawaikiyo'o*

Recognized and named, but no further data available.

Accipiter striatus   Sharp-shinned Hawk   *Kawaikiyo'o*

Recognized and named, but no further data available.

Aquila chrysaetos   Golden Eagle   *Asa'a'*

According to P.B., eagles nested on the limestone cliffs in the upper portion of Cataract Canyon. Eagle feathers were used during dances to ornament masks or combs (Cushing 1882).

If a man had a little baby at home, he must not touch an eagle. Should he even eat meat upon which an eagle had been feeding, the baby would have stomach trouble (Spier 1928). For this reason game was not left exposed.

In mythology Snake was said to have worn a downy red feather in his hair. In another myth, Eagle figured as a man.

Buteo jamaicensis   Red-tailed Hawk   *Cilkomi'i'*

Apparently not differentiated from the marsh hawk (*Circus cyaneus*).

Buteo regalis   Ferruginous Hawk   *Sikawwla'*

The Havasupai name applied to any *Buteo* hawk with a white tail. Since members of this species with red tails were not included, the scientific and native terminologies cannot be directly equated at this point. This large bird was particularly abundant in the Grand Canyon region in the fall and winter. The ceremonial use of its feathers was similar to that of the eagle.

Ferruginous hawks, which were rather tame and fairly easy to catch, were kept as pets. They were tied by one leg to a tree and fed lizards, rats, mice, or rock squirrels when available. If boys had been hunting the finches which endangered the peach crop, these, too, might be fed to the hawks. M.T. said that these pets were sometimes staked out in the gardens for scarecrows. If released near the house, these pet hawks would fly away and then return.

The wing feathers (M.T. specified the secondaries) were used to feather arrows. Tail feathers from the mature birds were used for headdresses in the same manner as those of the eagle.

Circus cyaneus   Northern Harrier   *Cilkomi'i'*

This bird was not differentiated from the red-tailed hawks (*Buteo jamaicensis*) or from those ferruginous hawks (*Buteo regalis*) that had red tails. The wing feathers might be used for arrows. They were looked upon as being more destructive than useful.

Falco mexicanus   Prairie Falcon   *Sokuula*

The wing feathers (M.T. said the secondary feathers only) were used on arrows. This bird was not always distinguished from the short-winged hawks (*Accipiter* spp.).

Falco peregrinus   Duck Hawk   *Icuta*

The feathers apparently were not used. B.B. described raising a young duck hawk obtained from a nest near Williams. It was fed the carcasses of mice and ground squirrels from which the skin had been removed. A "house" was built for the bird in a tree, or it was tied by a leg in the shade. This hawk was said to dive very fast and to cut off chickens' heads with its (knife-life) wings. If an expectant mother should hear this bird cry, her child might have the hawk's spirit, which would cause the child to sicken.

Falco sparverius   Sparrow Hawk   *Sinuuta*

A small hawk, often taken from the nest and raised as a pet. It was fed lizards. When full grown it would return, if freed, though eventually it returned permanently to the wild.

Order Galliformes

FAMILY PHASIANIDAE

Gallus gallus   Chicken   *Kowaako'o*

B.B. stated that the Havasupai obtained chickens from the Hopi "long ago." They were frequently raised for their eggs. The flesh, however, was seldom eaten, and chicken dinners at the school were unpopular. Some hen houses were built, but, in general, chickens were allowed to run wild except when they might endanger the growing crops. Occasionally they were fed corn. Several varieties were recognized and named by color. The name comes from the Spanish *gallo*.

| *Lophortyx gambelii* | Gambel's Quail | *Hima'a* |

Quail were abundant in the vicinity of the village at harvest time (Spier 1928). They were hunted with reed-shafted arrows with pointed wooden foreshafts. To prepare the birds for cooking, the feathers were pulled off and the entrails removed. The abdominal cavity was filled with small, hot stones, and the meat was placed on hot stones in a pit in the ground and covered. A fire was built on top, "just enough to heat it, but not enough to burn it." It took two or three hours for quail to cook. Sometimes it was buried under the hot ashes of a camp fire, and other times it was boiled, in which case the head and feet, as well as the entrails, were removed.

Quail meat was eaten infrequently; the eggs, however, were common in the Havasupai diet during the season when they could be found under the bushes near the village. The eggs, which were boiled or baked under the ashes of a fire, were the only wild bird eggs that were eaten.

At the time of his visit in 1881, Cushing (1882) described a boy's hair which was cut to look like the plume of a Gambel's Quail.

FAMILY MELEAGRIDIDAE

| *Meleagris gallopavo* | Merriam's Turkey | *'Iyaase'* |

Turkeys were hunted in the pine country to the west, near Pine Springs, and in the mountains to the east, near Flagstaff. In 1927 or 1928 some domestic birds were brought into the village by the Indians. These did considerable damage to the crops and were finally disposed of in the time-honored fashion.

Turkeys were cooked in pits lined with hot stones after the feathers, entrails, head, and legs had been removed. Apparently a fire was built over the pit. Four hours was said to be an adequate cooking time. P.B. said that the bird might be cut into pieces and boiled, but others denied this practice. The feathers were not used.

In mythology, Turkey was once a man. He was lazy, and when he found his wife had been unfaithful to him, he sent her back to Wren Man, who had a nice, warm house. She refused to go, so he flew up into a pine tree, leaving the poor woman alone in a snowstorm, and she froze to death. In the morning, when he built a fire near her, her body burst open and many different kinds of animals came out. These were attributed to her promiscuous habits. All the animals on the world's surface today are descended from these, her children.

Order Columbiformes

FAMILY COLUMBIDAE

Zenaida macroura	**Mourning Dove**	*Kuwii'i'*

These doves were abundant in the village when there were weed or crop seeds available. When they came to water, they were shot with bows and arrows. Ten or fifteen might be shot at one time. The feathers were removed and the birds buried in wet sand. A small fire was built on top of the sand, and in two hours they were said to be "pretty good eating." Though the informants told about such feasts with some glee, they were probably more children's activities than an important supply of food. Spier (1928) noted, for example, that doves were eaten infrequently.

Order Cuculiformes

FAMILY CUCULIDAE

Coccyzus americanus occidentalis	**Yellow-billed Cuckoo**	*Kapuu'u'*
Geococcyx californianus	**Roadrunner**	*Tekapuu'u'*

The Havasupai name for the roadrunner reflects a recognition of the relationship of this bird to *kapuu'u*, the cuckoo.

Order Strigiformes

FAMILY STRIGIDAE

Bubo virginianus	**Great Horned Owl**	*'Iyuu'u'*

Owl feathers were used to decorate dance masks. The owl was said to warn the Havasupai of approaching enemies or approaching death in any form. Sinyella (Little 1881) told of men hearing an owl hoot before an enemy raid.

In mythology, Owl was a quasi-human character who enabled the hero to escape his enemies by smoking a terrific quantity of tobacco in a pipe. In the resulting cloud of darkness the enemies became confused and began to fight each other, while the hero and the two heroines escaped. The name was derived from *yuu'u'* eye.

Otus kennicottii   Western Screech-Owl   *Kaqoqa*
It was said to be little bigger than a man's fist and had horns.

Order Apodiformes

FAMILY APODIDAE

Aeronautes saxatalis   White-throated Swift   *Wiqliita*
Not differentiated from swallows (Family Hirundinidae).

FAMILY TROCHILIDAE

Species Not Differentiated   Hummingbirds   *Miinmiine'*
Recognized and named, but no further data available.

Order Piciformes

FAMILY PICIDAE

Colaptes auratus cafer   Northern Flicker   *Kakuu'u'*
Boys used the feathers of this bird for arrows. In a myth, there came a great flood which covered the world with water and drowned out all life except this bird, which kept flying above the rising waters. Finally, as he clung to the heavens, the end of his tail got wet, and that is why the tip of his tail feathers are black.

Species Not Differentiated   Woodpeckers   *'i'iqsapeiiva'*
Apparently the Havasupai term had much the same connotation as the English term. It included the following species:

Colaptes chrysoides	Northern Flicker
Picoides pubescens	Downy Woodpecker
Picoides villosus	Hairy Woodpecker
Picoides tridactylus	Three-toed Woodpecker
Sphyrapicus varius	Yellow-bellied Sapsucker

In the name, *'i'i*- means "wood."

Order Passeriformes

FAMILY TYRANNIDAE

Myiarchus cinerascens   **Ash-throated Flycatcher**   *Tetapii'u'*
The identification was uncertain.

FAMILY HIRUNDINIDAE

Species Not Differentiated   **Swallows**   *Wiqliita*
Also not differentiated from the white-throated swift, *Aeronautes saxatalis*.

FAMILY CORVIDAE

Aphelocoma coerulescens   **Scrub Jay**   *Cascase*
The repeated syllable was characteristic of the language of the Havasupai, as well as that of the jays themselves.

Corvus corax   **Common Raven**   *Kasaqla'*
Ravens were said to eat frogs.

Cyanocitta stelleri   **Steller's Jay**   *Sa'ka'kwava*
The name, which was specific for this jay, means "talking birds," from *'icisa'a* bird and *ka'kwava* talking.

Gymnorhinus cyanocephalus   **Pinyon Jay**   *Qo'a'a'*
The name means "pinyon-bird," from *aqo'o* pinyon and *asa'a* bird.

FAMILY TROGLODYTIDAE

Catherpes mexicanus   **Canyon Wren**   *Tatiithee*

Salpinctes obsoletus   **Rock Wren**   *Tatiithee*
The habits of these birds were well known. E.U. differentiated the Rock Wren as *tatiith-seiiya*, meaning "gray wren," and the canyon wren as *tatiith-kwatha*. It is unlikely that these were generally recognized terms.

FAMILY MUSCICAPIDAE

Sialia currucoides	Mountain Bluebird	'*Icisa*'*havasuu*'*a*'
Sialia mexicana	Western Bluebird	'*Icisa*'*havasuu*'*a*'

The name, which applies to both species, means bluebirds, in which '*icisa*'*a* means "birds" and *havasuu*' means "blue" or "green."

Turdus migratorius	American Robin	*Tokapiila*'

Recognized and named, but no further data available.

FAMILY EMBERIZIDAE

Junco hyemalis	Slate-colored Junco	'*Icisa*'*hanapaca*'

Recognized and named, but no further data available.

Piranga ludoviciana	Western Tanager	*Ciqoocikaava*

Recognized and named, but no further data available.

Wilsonia pusilla	Wilson's Warbler	*Sakwatha*

The Havasupai name for Wilson's Warbler was often given in its full form, '*icisa*'*akwtha*, meaning "yellow birds." This term was used rather loosely and applied to any small, yellow bird, including some of those in the "warblers" group (see next entry).

Various Genera	"Warblers"	'*Ichisa*'*ka*'*kwava*

The name for warblers, though similar to that applied to the "talking birds"—the Steller's Jay (*Cyanocitta stelleri*)—apparently meant in this context "singing birds." A descriptive, rather than a specific, term, it was applied to a large and loosely defined group which included the following:

Carduelis psaltria	Lesser Goldfinch
Dendroica petechia (aestiva)	Yellow Warbler
Dendroica coronata	Yellow-rumped Warbler
Geothlypis trichas	Common Yellowthroat
Vermivora virginiae	Virginia's Warbler

Note that the Lesser Goldfinch is also included in the "small birds" group (see Family Fringillidae, below).

Various Genera   "Blackbirds"   *Ciqoo'o*
The Havasupai term *ciqoo'o* included the following birds:

Agelaius phoeniceus	Red-winged Blackbird
Euphagus cyanocephalus	Brewer's Blackbird
Molothrus ater	Brown-headed Cowbird
Xanthocephalus xanthocephalus	Yellow-headed Blackbird

FAMILY FRINGILLIDAE

Carpodacus mexicanus   **House Finch**   '*Aathaatha*'
These birds appeared in the Havasupai peach orchards in large flocks
when the peaches were ripening. They were formerly shot with bow
and reed arrows; later .22 rifles were used. The dead birds were often
fed to pet hawks.

HAVASUPAI TERMS FOR BIRDS THAT DO NOT
FIT INTO SCIENTIFIC TAXONOMIC CATEGORIES

Various Genera   "Gray Birds"   *Sa'oseiya*
This was a descriptive term which applied to a variety of birds,
including the following:

Icteria virens	Yellow-breasted Chat
Lanius ludovicianus	Loggerhead Shrike
Mimus polyglottos	Northern Mockingbird
Pheucticus melanocephalus	Black-headed Grosbeak

Various Genera   "Small Birds"   *Piith piith*
This indistinct term applied to a group of small birds of different
families which include the following:

Dendroica petechia	Yellow Warbler
Regulus calendula	Ruby-crowned Kinglet
Regulus satrapa	Golden-crowned Kinglet
Spinus carduelis	Lesser Goldfinch

CLASS MAMMALIA

Order Chiroptera

FAMILY VESPERTILIONIDAE

| *Species Not Differentiated* | Bats | *Cikapanyika* |

In a myth, Bat Man (or Men) rescues *hate'u'u* (the star Altair) from a high cliff. He was a noted polygamist. A group of stars (Hyades) was known as the Wives of the Bat. The bat was definitely not considered a bird. The name means "they who moved a man down." It can be broken into the following: *ci* those, *ka* who, *pa* man, *ni* down, *ka* do.

Order Lagomorpha

FAMILY LEPORIDAE

| *Lepus californicus* | **Desert Jackrabbit** | *'Akuula* |
| *Sylvilagus audubonii* | **Desert Cottontail** | *Halo'o'* |

These two rabbits were distinguished by sight and name. The jackrabbit was found in open-desert country, the cottontail in the canyons and pine country. Rabbits were an important food item, particularly during the winter season on the Plateau. Cushing (1882) said that "blood, intestines, even visceral glands and organs, as well as the half-digested vegetable matter from the stomach of the deer, antelope, and rabbit . . . [were] used for food. The liver is frequently eaten raw, immediately on the death of the animal." In 1941 informants did not specifically mention eating liver or other elements.

The skins were formerly of considerable importance. Cushing (1882) mentioned a breechcloth of rabbit skin. Large rabbit-skin blankets, *kuhuula*, were used as bedding; smaller ones were worn habitually by the women and, in very cold weather, by the men.

The ideal time for hunting rabbits was when there was deep snow, although the animals were also hunted when there was little or no snow. A prayer was said to Sun over the first rabbit killed each morning. As soon as the animal was killed, the whiskers were pulled off, it was raised to the lips and thrown toward the sun while blowing audibly on it. A fixed prayer was uttered, asking Sun to give the hunter lots of rabbits (P.B.).

The strings of rattles attached to women's belts were sometimes made of bone tubes cut from the leg bones of jackrabbits or cottontails (Spier 1928).

Order Rodentia

Rodents of various kinds were abundant in the vicinity of the village. While many of them were eaten, they were basically thought of as pests. Rodent-tight granaries were built to store the crops, particularly while the family was away during the winter. One of the great difficulties in harvesting the crop was to get the corn dry before the local rodents ruined it. Little smudges of dung were sometimes built near the drying corn to scare off the rodents (Spier 1928).

An unidentified, small rodent called *kootu'u'* was described as looking like a rat with a long body; it was said to have long toes and a short tail and to dig in the ground. It was found only on the Plateau. The skin of this rodent was removed and the body baked and dried, bones and all (M.T.). It was then pounded into fine powder and fed to women who desired children.

FAMILY SCIURIDAE

Cynomys gunnisoni   **Gunnison's Prairie Dog**   *Tuqsi'i*

This animal was a pest in the fields. In the myth in which the Squirrel brothers played a prominent part, Prairie Dog helped to dig the hole which led under Sun's house. Spier (1928) suggested that the name was derived from Spanish-American *tuza* (prairie dog), but it is more likely that it came from the Walapai *tuksi* or Yuma *takše* gopher.

Eutamias dorsalis   **Cliff Chipmunk**   *'Imuqwetha'*

Found in the vicinity of the village (Mearns 1907). Said by informants to be found on the South Rim. This animal was not eaten, nor was it a man in the mythological period.

Sciurus aberti   **Abert's Squirrel**   *'Imuqwethita*

This squirrel was never seen outside of the yellow-pine areas. It was not eaten. In a myth two Squirrel Men, who were brothers, were "pretty smart guys" (I.U.). In a series of matches, chiefly of an athletic nature but including successful copulation with a girl who possessed a toothed vagina, the brothers were victorious over the outraged Sun. Various localities were pointed out as scenes of some of the incidents in this story. Rain Tank, between Anita and Grand Canyon Station, was said to be the tank at which the brothers lived. There was some confusion regarding the second brother: it is possible that he was a different kind of squirrel, perhaps the Kaibab Squirrel from the North Rim (Spier 1928). The name can be broken down to the following: *imuqwetha'* chipmunk and *-ta* large.

Spermophilus lateralis   Golden-mantled Ground Squirrel   — — —

These were common in the yellow-pine country and either were not recognized or were confused with the rock squirrel.

Spermophilus variegatus   Rock Squirrel   *'Immilta*

They were plentiful in the vicinity of the village, where, during planting and harvest time, they were a serious pest (Mearns 1907). They were trapped, brought home and cooked by men, though the whole family ate them. Tobacco was stored in a sack made from the hide of this animal. The name means "large pocket gopher," from *'immile'* pocket gopher and *-ta* large.

FAMILY CRICETIDAE

Neotoma spp.   Woodrats   *'Ammalka*

Woodrats were found from the Havasupai village, where they were something of a pest to farmers, to the edge of the Grand Canyon. These animals gathered pinyon nuts and covered them with piles of sticks; these piles were looked for, as they eased the labor of gathering pinyon nuts.

Woodrats were eaten: the fur was singed and the entire animal baked in a hot pit. The entrails were not removed (P.B.). Sometimes the meat was boiled (P.B., M.T.).

A medicine called *'ammalka'thuca* consisted of a decoction of rat feces, which could be found in cracks in the rocks. This was given when a person failed to urinate or was constipated: "This will clean out the body" (E.U.). It was good medicine because "rodents eat all kinds of weeds" (B.B.). It was mild enough to be given to babies (E.U.).

Peromyscus maniculatus   Deer Mouse   *Awee'e*

Probably included several species, including *P. crinitus* and *P. truei*. P.B. thought the Hopi might eat them, but the Havasupai did not. In a myth, Snake and his people were camped one night near the enemy, and during the night they sent Mouse into the foreign camp. In the morning, their surprise attack was very successful, for all the bow strings of the enemy broke at the first touch, since Mouse had chewed them nearly, but not quite, through.

FAMILY GEOMYIDAE

Thomomys bottae   Botta's Pocket Gopher   '*Immile*'

These were found around the Grand Canyon Village. They were not eaten.

FAMILY ERETHIZONTIDAE

Erethizon dorsatum   Porcupine   *Kiitata*'

They were found in the yellow pines and in the pinyon trees. When one was located in a pinyon tree, a man would climb up and hit the animal on the head with a stick. A fire was built and the quills burned off. It was then taken to camp, where usually the men cooked it, but women might help.

Porcupine hair, *nymika*, was used to tie up a man's hair in a large knot at the back of his head, "like the Navajo" do.

The quills, *qwita qwita ka*, were not used (P.B., B.B., I.U.). Spier (1928) said, however, that colored quills were applied as decoration to the buckskin strip used to tie up the hair and to the top of the moccasin. The latter was a Hopi trait, and by 1941 was no longer customary with either the Hopi or the Havasupai.

In a myth, Porcupine killed a large deer (P.B.). *Kiitata*' means "he who has spines."

FAMILY CASTORIDAE

Castor canadensis   Beaver   '*Aniina*'

Undoubtedly at one time there were far more of these animals in the area than were found in 1941. B.B. spoke of seeing their tracks near Cameron. James (1900) said Beaver Falls was named "from the large number of beaver constantly at work there." P.B. and B.J. both spoke of them as living in this region. B.B. said they were trapped or shot with a rifle and the skins were sold to the Hopi. B.B. also said they were eaten, but P.B. and M.T. denied this. Beavers appear never to have been a very important resource.

Order Carnivora

FAMILY FELIDAE

Felis concolor   **Mountain Lion**   *Nymita*

Spier (1928) described in detail the tanning of the hide and the manufacture of a quiver, *nyipuwa*, from it. Because mountain lions were not often seen, such quivers were scarce and could be afforded only by the richer members of the group (Spier 1928).

In the manufacture of a bighorn-sheep horn spoon, grease of both mountain lion and bighorn sheep was rubbed into the boiled horn before it was shaped (Spier 1928).

Mountain lion flesh could not be eaten, "or even touched" (Spier 1928) by young married men or women when there were little babies in the family. The same applied to "the flesh of a deer slain by a mountain lion" (Spier 1928). Men with small children at home took special care not to leave a deer carcass exposed or even scraps of meat lying around which a mountain lion might touch. Should any of these various things happen, the babies' eyes would sink in, their bellies would ache, and diarrhea would ensue (Spier 1928); they might even die (D.I.).

In one myth Mountain Lion wanted snow to be "bread" for the people, but Coyote said no because "when the snow falls, they will go hunting rabbits." Another myth tells how Mountain Lion was responsible for Coyote's becoming a star.

The name comes from *nymi'i* bobcat and *-ta* large. Sometimes the Havasupai name for wolf was applied to the mountain lion, particularly in mythology. The origin of a hunting prayer was traced back to Mountain Lion and Wolf (Spier 1928).

*Felis sylvestris   **Domestic cat**   *Muuso'o'*

In 1881 Cushing (1882) saw six or eight domestic cats which were extravagantly prized by their possessors. The name was the same as that used by the Hopi, from the Spanish word *miz* cat.

Lynx rufus   **Bobcat**   *Nymi'i*

These animals, which were hunted for food, were fairly common in the vicinity of the Grand Canyon. P.B. described the hunting methods. After a big snow, they were tracked with dogs. The bobcat, afraid of the dogs, would climb a tree. A man then climbed after it and hit it on the head with a special hunting stick. This stick, called '*nyme-avia* (meaning "bobcat to beat") was made of cedar or oak and was shaped like a baseball bat. Just some men had these sticks. Other men might borrow them and give the owners a share of the cooked meat after the hunt. B.B. said a bobcat might be shot in the side with bow and arrow.

As with the mountain lion, young married people would not eat bobcat meat, nor would they touch the animal or eat meat which it had gnawed at or touched, for fear their young children would get sick or die.

Bobcat skins were saved and later tanned with the brains and marrow of the spine. Four to six skins were sewn together to make a blanket. P.B. spoke of making a soft collar from the fur, probably similar to those worn by some Hopi Kachinas. The femurs were made into tubes in which were kept a braided length of cotton which was used to catch the spark from the strike-a-light (B.B.). Similar tubes were sometimes hung as rattles from a woman's belt (Spier 1928).

A pair of femora, split in the plane of the trochanter head, was decorated with red paint on the interior and used as dice in a game called *sa'ak*.

The skull of the bobcat should not be broken. Care was taken to prevent this while cooking the meat. When the carcass was still around the house, one must be careful not to let the children play with it. If the skull should be broken or played with, heavy snows, rain, or wind would follow (M.T., B.B., P.B.).

The bobcat never appeared as a human figure in mythology. P.B., upon being questioned about this point, replied, "Never heard. They kill them—get skins to make blankets." This reply is interpreted to mean that at the time when other animals "were men," bobcat was hunted for his fur and, hence, could not have been one of those who were "human."

FAMILY CANIDAE

Canis familiaris   Dog   *Ahat*

Spier (1928) noted that Havasupai dogs were bred to be good hunters and were castrated. In 1941 informants generally agreed that dogs were not used to hunt deer, though Spier (1928) stated that they were used for that purpose. In 1941 some of the same informants who had aided Spier (E.I., P.B., B.B., D.I.) confirmed that dogs were used to hunt rabbits. E.I. stated that young dogs were taken out and shown rabbit tracks and thus trained specifically for this purpose. He said they were also trained to keep squirrels and birds off the fields (E.I.). James (1900) reported, "They are often tied out in the gardens and fruit patches to keep raccoons, foxes, and other predatory animals from destroying the fruit."

Dogs were called by name by many people, though apparently not all dogs were named (E.I.). In 1941 common names for dogs were "Curley," "Tommy," or "Trixie." Formerly, a person's dog, as well as his horse, was killed upon the master's death (Cushing 1882).

Canis latrans	Coyote	*Kathad*

Coyotes were tracked in the snow and killed with a club (Spier 1928). The meat was not ordinarily eaten, although if game was scarce it might be. "It has a strong odor which most people do not like, but I like it" (Mrs. B.J.). The animal came under the same food taboos as did wolves and mountain lions. Coyote skins were tanned and used for "gloves" (P.B., D.I., B.B.), robes, and bedding (Spier 1928). The skins were not used in dances, however, nor were they traded to the Hopi for such a purpose (Spier 1928).

Young animals were sometimes kept as pets. Cushing (1882) noted "beautiful little coyotes—fondled and petted—allowed a place at the family bowl even in preference to the women and children."

The Oregon-grape, *Berberis repens*, was used as medicine which Coyote Man told "his people" how to use for headache or upset stomach. It was known as *kathad' iisma' a* Coyote medicine. The wild tobacco on the plateau was attributed to Coyote. A boy could not smoke until he had killed a coyote. The name of the coyote occurred in several plant names with the implication that coyote's plants were not just as they should be.

The Havasupai attitude toward Coyote Man was difficult to define. It was essentially an attitude of affection, in spite of the fact that many afflictions, from incest to weather, were attributed to his foolish behavior. To say that he was an important mythological character would be to radically understate his role. He was the unheroic hero who fumbled through tale after tale, usually losing his life at the climax of each one.

Spier (1928) stated that scouts communicated with each other by calling in imitation of owls or coyotes.

| *Canis lupus* | Gray Wolf | *Hatakwila* |

Wolves were probably never abundant in the Grand Canyon region, but occasionally an individual might have wandered into the area. The Havasupai interest in the creature was maintained, to a considerable extent, through mythology, but even here, the wolf was occasionally confused with the mountain lion. The food taboos for parents of young children that applied to the mountain lions applied also to wolves, though elsewhere P.B. and B.B. said that the meat was never eaten. The skins, three of which would make a blanket (B.B.), were saved.

A plant called *hatakwila' iisma'a* wolf medicine (*Frasera speciosa*) was used to clear the bowels and sometimes to induce vomiting (Spier 1928).

Wolf, like Coyote and Mountain Lion, was once a man.

| *Urocyon cinereoargenteus* | Gray Fox | *Qoqot* |

These animals were sometimes killed with a special hunting stick, as was the bobcat. The meat was not eaten, and the restrictions previously outlined for mountain lions and other animals also applied to foxes (P.B.). The skins were carefully saved and, for the most part, sold to the Hopi, for whom they were an important part of ritual attire. Formerly the Havasupai also wore fox skins, like the Hopi, with the heads tucked into the back of their belts.

In a myth, two Fox Men, who were brothers, succeeded in releasing a large number of their contemporaries from the giant bird, *miyakiu*.

FAMILY PROCYONIDAE

| *Bassariscus astutus* | Ringtail Coatimundi | *'Amma'lka'ta* |

The ring-tailed cat, as it was sometimes called, combined the tail of a raccoon and the body and fur of a cat with the feet and disposition of a squirrel. It was chiefly nocturnal. B.B. said that the ringtail was killed for food by trapping it under a flat, stone deathfall. This was probably not a common practice, for P.B. denied eating it, and M.T. made no mention of it. P.B. included it in his list of animals that, like mountain lion, could not be touched or eaten by parents of young children. The name means "large woodrat."

Procyon lotor   Raccoon   *Nanthe*

Raccoons occurred frequently in the village (James 1900). P.B. said
they came to the village at night to steal corn and figs. They were
eaten, but not often. B.B. said that they were baked in a pit in the
earth (probably in much the same fashion as described in Chapter 4
for other game animals). Although the animal is fairly common and
was clearly described, data on the terminology were confusing: B.B.
called it *nanthe*; others called it '*apiina*', the name applied to beaver.

FAMILY URSIDAE

Ursus americanus   Black Bear   *Nakoo'o*

These large animals were common in the mountains to the south, and
could occasionally be found along the south rim of the Grand Canyon. B.B. said it was not safe to try to kill one unless one was
mounted on horseback. He says five or six stone-pointed arrows
would be required. He also said it would be either boiled or baked in
an earth pit. Blankets might be made from the hide (B.B., P.B.). Spier
(1928) reported that one of his informants, named Sinyella, indicated
that the Havasupai did not know what to do with the hide and
eventually threw it away. Another time he said a bear hide was sold
to a white man.

FAMILY MUSTELIDAE

Mephitis mephitis   Striped Skunk   *Hwiwoo'o*

Spilogale gracilis   Western Spotted Skunk   *Hwiwoo'o*

The western spotted skunk was found in the Grand Canyon and the
striped skunk on the Plateau. They were not differentiated by the
Havasupai. The bite was said to be poisonous, although D.I. and B.B.
were inclined to believe that this was a white man's idea.

Taxidea taxus   Badger   *Amuhwaa'a*

Men, not women, hunted and killed badgers by hitting them on the
head. After the skin and the entrails were removed, the cavity was
filled with hot stones and placed in a hot pit. The pit was then
covered with pinyon and (probably moist) earth, and a fire was built
on top. Men or women cooked this meat (M.T.). The badger was put
into the cooking pit in the morning and removed in the evening.

The skin was tanned and used as a sack to hold tobacco, etc. (P.B.) or to make shoes (M.T.). During the interview, M.T. restrained her daughter from petting the fur. "Young kids should not touch it—it makes their hair fall. It has the same effect upon older people, so they wash afterwards" (M.T.).

Order Perissodactyla

FAMILY EQUIDAE

Equus caballus   Horse   *Vo'olo'o*

The Havasupai have had horses for a long time. Garcés (Coues 1900) found horses and cattle among the Havasupai in 1776. They claimed to have received them from the Hopi. Spier (1925) quotes Sinyella (an informant), talking of his boyhood sometime before 1850: "At that time we did not have many horses to ride; perhaps our family had only one." Cushing (1882) spoke of the introduction of horses "within the last few years."

By 1941 the Havasupai owned a sizeable number of horses. They traded horses to the Navajo and the Walapai and to whites. They were excellent horsemen and consistently made very creditable showings in direct competition with other tribes at rodeos.

In certain areas in the vicinity of Beaver Canyon the Havasupai owned wild horses, which were smaller than normal. It was claimed that these were the descendents of prehistoric forms which had been isolated in an inaccessible canyon by a landslide. This was, of course, not true. There was no such valley, and the horses were of historic origin, dwarfed as the result of poor feed, little water, isolation, and inbreeding (Franse 1938b). These horses were called *olo'oqlace*, little horses.

In 1941 the Havasupai pastured their horses during winter and spring on the Plateau or on the Esplanade. In late June or July, when the water holes and springs on the Plateau began to dry out, the horses were sometimes brought down into Cataract Canyon, where food and water was available.

Horses were used to plow the fields and for freighting supplies and tourists in and out of the canyon. A man usually had several strings of horses which he alternated every few trips. Horses were formerly used to hunt pronghorn and in 1941 were used extensively during the deer season.

Over the years horses and horsemanship became important factors in Havasupai economy. There was a virtual migration to Flagstaff for the Indian rodeo. Later in the season, during the Peach dance, a local rodeo was held in the village to which the Walapai, Mohave, and an occasional Navajo came. The latter were not unwelcome, but they found no cheering section to aid their morale. In contrast to the Apache, the chief interest of the Havasupai was in horse racing, broncbusting, and similar displays of horsemanship, rather than in calf roping, bulldogging, and steer riding. The Havasupai were definitely horsemen, not cattlemen.

E.U. said that you "sing" when you break in a wild horse. The songs which were sung were designed to bring well-being to horse and rider.

Formerly, when it was customary to burn the dead along with his or her personal property, a favorite horse or horses were killed. The animal was killed by tying a strip of wet buckskin around the neck. This shrank as it dried, strangling the animal (James 1903). In 1941 a rag was tied over the horse's eyes and it was either shot or hit on the forehead with an axe. James (1903) said that the animal's body was burned. (Spier (1928) thought that practice doubtful and added that sometimes the horse was pushed over the cliff. E.U. said that in 1941, when cremation was no longer being practiced, the horse was buried in a separate grave. The saddle was usually left on the horse, but it was not slashed or cut as is the custom among the Navajo. According to B.B., a saddle might be buried with the man.

Horsehair, arranged to look like the dancer's own hair, was once attached to masks worn in a dance, but this custom was discontinued some years ago (Spier 1928). Dorsey (1903) mentioned horsehair loops on each side of the carrying basket to which the tumpline was attached.

In a gesture signifying horseback riding, the index and middle finger of the right hand were extended, separated at an angle, and pointed downward. The resulting inverted "V" was then set astride the extended fingers of the left hand.

The shoulder blade of a horse was used for scraping the sand into ridges for irrigation and for scraping out weeds in the agricultural fields. This tool was held in the hands, not hafted (Spier 1928). Horses were occasionally eaten in the past, as described in Chapter 3.

Horses were owned only by men and were branded in the typical

southwestern fashion. Brands, too, were owned by the men; sometimes several men, usually relatives, owned a single brand. The
Havasupai word for "horse" comes from the Spanish word *caballo*
horse. The word for horse manure was *vo'olo'- colka* and for "pinto"
(spotted horse) *vo'olo'-nuda*.

Equus hemionus	Burro	*Muulo'o*

The Havasupai have had burros for many years. E.U. says that burro
meat was once eaten. The animals were used to pack firewood and
field produce, but few people owned burros in 1941; it seemed that
the horse had replaced them. The Havasupai did not own any mules,
although there was a mule at the sub-agency and a large number at
the Grand Canyon. Mules were also called *muulo'o*.

Order Artiodactyla

FAMILY BOVIDAE

Antilocapra americana	Pronghorn	*'Ama'ule*

Around the turn of the century the pronghorn was abundant in the
lightly forested open plains south of the Grand Canyon. After 1890
they began to decrease in numbers, and by 1907 they had virtually
disappeared* from this region (McGreggor 1935). Pronghorn hunting
techniques are discussed in Chapter 3.

It was thought that if a person swallowed the hair of a pronghorn,
he would die.

Within the historic period, pronghorns were hunted by groups of
men on horseback with bow and arrow. A man with a poor or tired
horse might ask another hunter on a fresh horse to get an animal for
him. In this case the killer retained the hide, though the meat was all
given to the man making the request (E.U.). Using horses probably
made pronghorn hunting more feasible.

Bison bison	American bison	*Mthi'*

The buffalo was probably known to the Havasupai largely through
hearsay from the Paiute and the Ute. Spier (1928) stated that buffalo

---

*In 1985 these animals were once again seen south of the Grand Canyon.

skins were obtained from the Hopi in trade. In a myth, Coyote committed incest with his daughter. The daughter returned in tears to her mother. In shame, they attempted to turn into various other animals and finally became buffaloes. The Havasupai cited this myth as the origin of incest. One informant mentioned reading in a newspaper of a case of incest in Chicago. His comment was, "That's where they get it. Coyote did it."

Bos taurus   Cattle   *Wakasi'i*

When Garcés visited the Havasupai in 1776 he found cattle that they had obtained from the Hopi. He suspected from the brands that they were stolen from Spanish missions (Coues 1900). Cushing said that in 1881 they had no cattle (Cushing 1882). In 1941 cattle were individually owned. The largest holder had less than sixty head, and most owners held less than ten head. In general, a man owned about three times as many horses as he did cattle. In 1941 the Havasupai owned between two hundred and three hundred head, and at that time there was considerable interest in a cattle roundup—men were even leaving paid labor in the village to go on it.

Cattle were pastured on the Plateau, where tanks provided water during most of the year. During the hot months of the summer, when these tanks were low or dry, the cattle were pastured in the upper end of Cataract Canyon, where there were permanent springs and some forage. The Havasupai term comes from the Spanish word *vaca* cow.

Capra hircus   Goats   *Suvaado'o*

Goats were introduced by S. M. McGowan around 1893 while he was on the Havasupai reservation. When he left to become superintendent of the Phoenix Indian School, the goats were killed off and forgotten (Arizona Graphic 1899). D.I. and E.U. denied that the Havasupai had ever had any goats.

Ovis aries   Sheep   *Kanelo'o*

The Havasupai had few, if any, sheep.

Ovis canadensis   Bighorn Sheep   *Amu'u'*

Although by 1941 they were exceedingly rare and were no longer hunted, formerly they had been quite abundant in the Grand Canyon area as well as the vicinity of Havasupai Village itself (Spier 1928). In former times sheep were occasionally shot near the village (Spier 1928), but they were usually hunted in the canyons above the village and to the east. Sometimes the hunters wore a disguise consisting of a stuffed ewe's head, with horns made of stuffed buckskin, and a buckskin hide colored with ashes (Spier 1928). At other times the bighorns were driven past places where hunters waited in ambush or they were driven directly over a cliff (Spier 1928). P.B. indicated such a point along the cliffs in the upper reaches of Cataract Canyon.

The meat was eaten, and sinew for bowstrings was obtained from the hind leg and back. While Spier (1928) specified the leg, P.B. said this was too stiff, and said to take it from the back.

Though the wool was not used, the hide was considered very strong and was made into braided ropes. S.J. described how men were let down on one of these ropes to get salt from a cave. The entire hide was made into a bag in which to store seeds and other things. Quivers might be made from the hide of young sheep, but these were considered inferior to those made of mountain lion hide (Spier 1928).

Lard of bighorn sheep was rubbed into the wood of a bow after it had been shaped. Bighorn sheep grease was worked in the hands and rubbed on the hair to make it shine. This grease might also be rubbed on the freshly pierced earlobe of an infant to help ease the pain (Spier 1928).

Bighorn sheep hooves were sometimes made into rattles and hung from a woman's belt (Spier 1928).

Perhaps the most important aspect of bighorn sheep, other than its immediate food value, was the horn, from which spoons were made. A spoon was hacked and trimmed into the shape wanted, soaked (E.U. said boiled), and buried in wet sand from three to six nights or until it was fairly soft. Then it was warmed at the fire and rubbed with the grease of mountain lion and bighorn sheep. The handle was bent to the desired angle, and the bowl, shaped and wedged open with a stick, was filled with dirt and laid aside to harden (Spier 1928). There seems to have been a variety of these utensils, but because they were so frequently buried with the dead, by 1941 they had largely disappeared. The most common form was a deep-bowled ladle, which was used in cooking. Continued use in hot liquids frequently relaxed the bowl to its original shape (Spier 1928). These spoons were often traded to the Hopi. M.M. also spoke of a horn cup from which people drank. These probably were little more than individual variations in the use of a pliable raw material.

The constellation Orion was called "bighorn sheep," although it was also said to represent several other game animals and the Animal Men hunting them.

Mythology recounts how Wolf made a baby by putting abalone shell into a water hole. Subsequently the child grew up and, after several adventures, secured two wives. When Wolf demanded one, the boy went off and became a bighorn sheep. His hair turned into horns, and the curly surface of the sheep's horn was pointed out as being due to the texture of the boy's hair.

FAMILY CERVIDAE

Odocoileus hemionus   **Mule Deer**   *Aqwaka*

Deer were found in the wooded areas east and west of Cataract Canyon along the south rim of the Grand Canyon and in the mountains across the open plains to the south. Formerly they were of far less importance than pronghorns and bighorn sheep, but with the disappearance, for all practical purposes, of these game animals, the deer took on increasing importance. Deer were still hunted in 1941, but in accordance with federal and state laws. The open season was observed, and no deer were killed on National Park lands. The participation in the white man's hunting patterns went beyond mere geographical and seasonal restrictions by including the use of cars, horses, guns, etc. E.U. told of running down a big buck on horseback.

P.B. said that while hunting, a man should put red paint on his face and should not eat meat, but only corn and mescal. Sinyella (an informant) told Spier (1928) of a magical procedure involving the burning of deer droppings and marking the face of each hunter with the ashes, followed by a prayer to Sun, made by the chief. This procedure was drawn from a myth in which Mountain Lion and Wolf ordained that it should be so. It would appear that this custom was practiced particularly when hunting parties were large or when game was scarce.

A calculus from the paunch of a deer was said to help the hunter approach deer, antelope, or bighorn sheep without being noticed (Spier 1928). Disguises similar to those described for pronghorn and bighorn sheep were sometimes employed, using branches for horns (Spier 1928). In addition, deer hunters often decoyed deer with a sound "like a baby deer," made by blowing across a folded leaf of the blue pentstemon. M.T. said, "The leaf was placed in the mouth like a harmonica." Deer were shot with bows and wood-shafted arrows with stone or metal points, and dogs were used to track wounded deer over hard ground (Spier 1928).

Deer which had been struck down by a mountain lion might also be taken for food, although there was a food restriction on such meat for the parents of young children. Cushing (1882) said that the half-digested contents of the deer's stomach were used for food and that the liver was frequently eaten raw, immediately upon the death of the animal. B.B. denied this practice; it may be an old pattern which had been abandoned by 1941.

Deer were usually skinned and the meat cut up and divided before the hunters returned to camp. Unless there was an abundance of meat, it was usually all consumed within a few days. If there was a surplus, it was cut into strips and dried. The brains and marrow from the spinal canal were collected at the time the deer was killed, for use in tanning (Spier 1928).

Buckskin was an important element in intertribal trade. Not only did the Havasupai produce it, they received it in trade, already tanned. It might be said that the Havasupai were the center of trade in buckskin in the area from the Colorado to the Río Grande. Cushing (1882) said the Havasupai had unrivaled celebrity for their buckskin. This fame was due, perhaps, to their close proximity to a large supply of game, rather than to the superiority of their product. Tanned deer hides were made into skin bags, the hoop for the hoop-and-pole game, and shields for warfare, and cut deer-hide strips were often braided into ropes.

The sinew from the deer was removed, hung on a tree to dry, and then stored. When sinew was wanted, the desired amount was split off and soaked in water to soften it. The bow string was made of two- or, preferably, three-ply sinew cord (three-ply was used for hunting, two-ply for playing around). Since one length was not long enough to reach across the bow, several lengths of sinew had to be combined by overlapping the ends about two inches. These overlappings were staggered; if they were not, or if a knot was used, the finished string would break. P.B. demonstrated how the overlapping strands were rolled together: the three component threads were held in the left hand while a twist was applied with a downward motion of the right palm pressed firmly against the right leg. The finished cord was then dried in the sun.

Deer sinew was used to add elasticity to the bow itself. Spier (1928) has given an excellent description of the manufacture of these sinew-backed bows. Sinew was also used on arrows to attach feathers, to strengthen the fore-end of the reed stem, and to attach the arrowhead. Other uses included sewing moccasins, attaching the crosspieces to a cradleboard, attaching feathers to string or pegs for hair ornaments, and any other situation where strong, thin "thread" was required.

Deer fat was sometimes mixed with red face paint; it was also mixed with the strong native tobacco to make a cooler smoke.

In addition to meat, hide, and sinew, the Havasupai used many other parts of the deer. For example, antlers furnished picks for digging clay and for lithic flaking. The ball for shinney was stuffed with deer fur, and dewclaw rattles were sometimes fastened to the hoop of the cradleboard (Spier 1928) or to the neck loop or belt of a woman's dress. In the past, women's dresses included jinglers of deer eyes. These decorations were prepared by cutting a tiny hole to drain the fluid within, drying the eyes, and then inserting a kernel of corn and tying the aperture (Spier 1928).

In mythology, deer always appeared as an animal, never as a man. The name means "he who has horns" or "the horned one."

Cervus canadensis	**Elk**	*Qwakata*

These huge animals were found only in the mountains to the south. They have not been hunted for some time. *Cervus canadensis merriami* became extinct about 1884. This area has been restocked with *Cervus canadensis nelsoni*. Elk meat was eaten and the skin tanned for moccasins, gloves, and probably for dresses and shirts (B.B.). Elk was mentioned in a myth, apparently as an animal. The name comes from *aqwaka* deer and *-ta* large.

14. The Plant Kingdom

Botanical collections were made in the Grand Canyon area in 1941, with the permission and cooperation of the National Park Service. Complete sets of these collections were placed on file at the Herbarium of the Museum of Northern Arizona and at the Herbarium of the Grand Canyon Natural History Association.

The knowledge of the botany of this area was far from complete in 1941, and the classifications of many species were a matter of debate. In contrast to the Hopi, the Havasupai did not name or recognize a large number of local species. Only the plant species which were significant to the Havasupai are discussed in any detail within this chapter.

There were a number of steps in the ethnobotanical field work. The first step was to collect specimens of the local flora, preferably in the presence of an informant. The plant was placed in a plant press and notes were taken for the botanical and ethnological records. Either at the time of collection or later, when it was possible to sit down and be protected from the wind, the plant or plants would be discussed with the informant. As a general rule, the native name of a botanical species was not established until at least a half dozen consistent identifications by as many informants were obtained, using at least two different specimens of the same species. After the specimens were identified, an ethnographic interview followed to discuss the uses and significance of the plant.

Plants which were unidentifiable to the informants in the dried state were usually the same plants which were not recognized in the field.

SPORE-BEARING PLANTS

——— Mosses, Lichens, Algae, etc. *Hamusukwaala*

This name was applied to any green growth of a nondescript nature growing under or near water. Moss growing on rocks was called *awi'-hamusukwaala* "rock moss." Moss growing on trees was called *'i'i'-hamusukwaala*.

Usnea spp. **Old Man's Beard** *Aqoyavinymi'i*

Occasionally grew on trees in the higher altitudes along the South Rim. The plant was collected, burned to an ash, and rubbed on sores to dry them out (P.B., M.M.). The name came from *aqo'o* pinyon and *yavinymi'i* whiskers.

FAMILY AGARICALES

Species Not Differentiated **Mushrooms** *Vuka'nyace*

P.B. cautioned against touching any mushroom which was shedding black spores, lest the black dust get in the eyes and make them sore or even cause blindness.

FAMILY EQUISETACEAE

Equisetum hiemale **Horsetail** *'Iwila'ata'*

This grew along the edges of the river near the village. Children pulled the joints apart and produced a whistling sound by blowing across them as one blows across the mouth of a bottle (D.I., Mrs. B.J.). The name means "long, cylindrical, spine-like."

FAMILY POLYPODIACEAE

Adiantum capillus-veneris **Maidenhair Fern** *Aha'yavinymi'i*

These ferns grew near the village during spring. The name translates as "water whiskers." Occasionally the meadowrue (*Thalictrum fendleri*) was confused with this fern.

SEED PLANTS

FAMILY PINACEAE

Pinus edulis	**Pinyon**	*Aqo'o*
Pinus monophylla	**Singleleaf**	*Aqo'o*

The single-leaf pinyon occurred frequently in the study area and differed from *Pinus edulis* only in that it had one instead of two leaves.

Pinyon wood was used in much the same fashion as that of the juniper: for firewood and house construction. E.U. pointed out, however, that pinyon wood made a better fire and left better coals for cooking than juniper. The wood was also used to make the knife for trimming mescal heads.

When porcupine, bobcat, or badger was cooked in an earth pit, sprigs of pinyon were placed in the pit with the animal. This was said to improve the taste of the cooked meat.

Pinyon gum, *anaiya*, was melted near a fire and applied to a cut on man or horse. E.U. said that pinyon gum was used in the paint used on the base of arrows. Spier (1928) stated that pinyon pitch was liberally daubed on the buckskin bindings of cradleboards. The gum was also used to waterproof basketry water jugs and basketry drinking cups. Melted gum was similarly used to plug a leaky canteen or other container (E.U.).

Pinyon nuts were by far the best-known product of the tree. Unfortunately, the crop was usually very light and a good harvest could be expected only once in several years. In the seasons when the crop was good, everyone was busy collecting the nuts. Martha, age three, was pointed out as being old enough to pick pinyon nuts. In good years, children were excused from the school in the village to help with the harvest.

In September the cones were picked green, before they opened, and placed on a bed of coals. The cones opened from the heat and the nuts were obtained. In October and November the cones opened naturally and the nuts fell to the ground, where they were picked up. Whole families took part in the collecting of pinyon nuts. P.B. said his family could get as much as fifty pounds a day, and E.U. said a family might gather from six to twenty sacks of nuts in a season.

Formerly they were an important food source. In 1941 they were sold in considerable quantities to stores near the reservation where they brought nine or ten cents per pound.

Various localities were known as good pinyon sections, and camps were made there during the pinyon harvests. The word for pinyon gum, *anaiya*, may have been derived from an older Yuman term for mesquite gum (*anaala* mesquite). The word for cone was '*qopai*, for needle '*qo-theq*, and for dead (pinyon) tree '*qo-pii'i*.

Pinus ponderosa	Western Yellow Pine	*Hwaale*

Found only in the high part of the Plateau in such areas as the Grand Canyon Village. The cones might be placed on a blanket and pounded with sticks to free the nuts, which were then roasted and eaten like pinyon nuts (M.T.). P.B. denied that the nuts were eaten.

The Walapai were called "yellow pine people," *hwaal-pai*.

Pseudotsuga menziesii	Douglas Fir	*Kathadavuhe'e*

A few of these trees grew below the canyon rim near Grand Canyon Village, but they were most abundant on the San Francisco Peaks to the south. They were important in Hopi ceremonials as symbols of rain. The Havasupai apparently at one time used branches of this tree in a manner similar to, and in imitation of, the Hopi. E.U. said that the leaves were good medicine. In winter they were boiled and given to the sick. The name can be broken down into the following two words: *kathad* coyote and *he'i'* tail.

FAMILY CUPRESSACEAE

Juniperus osteosperma	Utah Juniper	'*Icoqa*

Juniper wood was very important as a source of firewood during the winter seasons, when the people lived on the Plateau. The winter houses on the Plateau were built of juniper logs and brush and covered with dirt. The pole of the hoop-and-pole game might be made of juniper (S.J.).

The bark was frequently confused by those unfamiliar with the Southwest with that of the cliff-rose, *Cowania* (Whiting 1938). Juniper bark was crushed and used for tinder (E.U.), particularly with the fire drill (M.T.). The crushed bark might also be twisted into a rope, tied at intervals with yucca, and wrapped into a coil, the free end of which was set on fire and kept smoldering by blowing on it at intervals. Fire could be carried in this fashion from early dawn until noon (E.U.). This "slow match" was called 'o'ho'kwiitia' (from 'o'o'o fire and -kwi to twist).

Bark was commonly put on the top of the brush covering of the winter houses to keep the dirt from falling through (P.B.). Spier (1928) mentioned crushed cedar bark used as a stopper for the basketry water bottle. He also mentioned bark dolls for little girls (it is possible that these were made of cliff-rose bark).

Green juniper branches were used singly or together with other plants as a cure for colds.

Juniper berries ripen in the fall. The Havasupai may have picked the berries off the ground, but more often they collected small branches, laid them on a blanket, and beat them with a stick to free the berries, which then might be dried in the sun and stored for use in the winter. When they were to be used, they were pounded or ground on a milling stone and then soaked in water for a couple of hours until the seeds fell to the bottom. The pulp was squeezed out and thrown away, and the remaining liquid was served as a drink. P.B. said to add a little sugar; like most Havasupai, he did not particularly like this drink but thought that the Walapai and Navajo did.

Kitner (1929) reported a belief to the effect that the Havasupai would live as long as the dwarfed juniper continued to grow from the top of the rock pinnacles towering over the village. No mention of this was made by any of the informants in 1941. The mythological significance of these rocks was vastly overrated, and this belief remained doubtful.

The Havasupai also occasionally came into contact with the one-seeded juniper, *J. monosperma,* which was abundant to the south and east.

FAMILY EPHEDRACEAE

Ephedra viridis   **Mormon Tea**   *Cimuwaiya*

Other species, such as *E. fasciculata, E. nevadensis,* and *E. torreyana* were found within the Havasupai range, and it is doubtful if they were distinguished by the Havasupai. They were common in the canyon and at lower elevations on the Plateau.

The upper portions of *Ephedra* were collected, put into a coffee pot with cold water, and brought to a boil. The tea was allowed for boil for not over two minutes; if boiled longer, it would become bitter.

P.B. said it tasted better when made during the fall months. This drink was a well-known substitute for coffee.

Spier (1928) said that the stems were dried in bundles for storage. The plant was thought to have medicinal properties. A handful of twigs was used to brush spines off prickly pear fruit. The name means "things to become warm."

FAMILY TYPHACEAE

Typha domingensis Cattail *Hamusu ' iiv*

Very bedraggled specimens were seen near the spring above the village and below Mooney Falls. This plant may once have been more abundant than it was in 1941. Until better material can be located, the species must remain in doubt.

The stalk was sometimes used to make toy arrows. The stalk and leaves were used in thatching houses. E.U. said that the pollen used to be used as a face paint. The ripe fruiting heads were eaten "like corn."

FAMILY GRAMINEAE

There were a great many grasses in Havasupai territory. As is true of this group everywhere, they were exceedingly abundant both in numbers and species, and, with a few exceptions, it was difficult for the average person to distinguish them. The terminology of grasses among any people, civilized or primitive, was therefore apt to be confused and inconsistent. The Havasupai were no exception. Many of the grass names obtained were descriptive terms evolved for the occasion; others were so broad in their application as to be practically meaningless. Unfortunately, it never became clear at any time during the field work whether or not this understandable confusion in terminology carried over into actual usage. Apparently, most of the Havasupai women of a generation or two ago, particularly when faced with a food shortage, went into the fields and collected grass seeds. It did not matter whether they were of one species or several.

Agropyron smithii Wheatgrass *Kumpammka ' iwil*

M.T. called *Agropyron smithii* by this Havasupai name, which means "grasshopper grass." She also applied this name to *Dactylis glomerata*, an introduced grass not previously reported in the state of Arizona. It was somewhat doubtful if she had ever seen it previously. Upon another occasion M.T. gave the name '*iwilakumpammka*' to *Stipa comata*.

Bouteloua spp.   Grama Grasses   '*Iwila*'*hataka*

Many of the grasses belonging to this genus were characterized by a relatively linear, frequently curved flower cluster set at a rather sharp angle to the stem, something like a very narrow flag. The name, applied rather consistently to all members of this genus, was said to refer to the appearance of the stem: "stem go up in hook" (cf. *halaka* hooked). The name was also applied to *Muhlenbergia porteri*, which vaguely resembles some of the *Bouteloua* species.

Cynodon dactylon   Bermuda Grass   '*Iwilathapita*

Two sacks of seed were washed down Cataract Creek at the time of the big flood in 1910. After the flood this grass came up all over the cultivated area; it has been a great drawback to native cultivation, as it is exceedingly difficult to eradicate.

Koeleria cristata   June Grass   '*I*'*el*

It was very difficult to tell from the conflicting data at hand to what species or group of species this name was applied. In any case, the grass or grasses included in this category by the Havasupai were an important food. M.M. said the plant looked like wheat and grew two or three feet high on side walls of the canyon. The fruiting heads were gathered in the fall and rubbed between the palms so that the seeds dropped into a basket (M.T.). The seeds were stored in blankets or bags of skin in caves (M.T.).

Oryzopsis hymenoides   Indian Millet   *Umsla*'*a*

Traditionally an important food grass. Attached to the base of the seeds were little bunches of fine hairs which had to be removed before the seeds were eaten. This grass was formerly much more abundant than it was in 1941. By this time livestock grazed it so that it did not come to maturity, and it was very difficult to find in sufficient quantities to make it worth collecting for human food.

Phragmites communis   Reed, Carrizo   *Ata*'*a*

Although reeds were not observed growing in the Grand Canyon area, E.U. reported seeing them at both Phantom Ranch and Cataract

Canyon. These reeds were used for arrowshafts, *apa'ata'a* (*apa'a* arrow, *ata'a* reed). Mats (*'ita'kwiva*) for drying yucca fruit pulp, baked mescal, peaches, or figs were sometimes made of reeds. These were held together with deerskin thongs or sinew twined through the reeds at half a dozen points (Spier 1928). Pipe stems were made from sections of reed (E.U., D.I.).

Poa fendleriana   Muttongrass   *Amowate*

One of the familiar species in the bluegrass genus. Common in the Plateau and upper portions of the side canyons, muttongrass ripened from early summer till August and was collected in June, July, and August. It was formerly very abundant and was an important food. A group of women would go together to collect the seeds.

Tridens pulchellus   Fluff Grass   *Iwilathatapa*

E.U. said that this grass was boiled and the liquid drunk as a laxative. It grew on the Plateau and was used occasionally. Other informants failed to recognize the specimen, and the data, therefore, remain doubtful. The name means "grass-gray."

*Triticum aestivum   Wheat   *Ape*

This plant was apparently not cultivated by the Havasupai, although they were familiar with it and used commercial wheat flour extensively.

*Zea mays   Corn   *Tiyace*

The word for corn means "from seed." Havasupai corn was very similar to the varieties raised by the Hopi, although it lacked the large range of color variations. Varieties which were present in 1941 were badly intermixed.

Both the Havasupai and the Hopi raised a quantity of a long-seasoned white corn that often had an admixture of red. It was used as a basic staple for winter storage. In addition, both tribes raised a short-seasoned, quick-maturing blue variety for early eating. Although some other color varieties were raised, they did not have the special cultural significance for the Havasupai that they had for the Hopi. It was clearly evident that varieties were constantly being obtained from neighboring agricultural tribes and, to a lesser extent, from non-Indians. For a long period of time mutual borrowing had occurred between the Hopi and the Havasupai. In addition, there were varieties grown in 1941 which originally had been obtained from the Walapai. A small variety—with ears about five inches long—had come by trade from the Mohave through the Walapai (Spier 1928). Such borrowings were stimulated by local catastrophes, such as the 1910 flood. Accounts of crop failure among the Pueblos relate how the Hopi and even the Zuni visited the Havasupai in search of food.

FAMILY CYPERACEAE

Scirpus spp.   **Bulrushes**   *Hamusu'iiv'puuta'puuta*

Although not observed in 1941, *Scirpus olneyi* was reported growing in Cataract Canyon in the vicinity of the village by the river by Deaver and Haskell (1955). Children sometimes braided it to make a whip. In the name, *hamusu'iiv* means "cattail" (*Typha domingensis*), and *-puuta'-puuta'* means "long and cylindric."

FAMILY JUGLANDACEAE

*Carya illinoensis   **Pecan**   *Kwecikaakece*

These trees were first planted by the resident Indian agent some time before 1925 (P.B.). In 1941 a number of fine large trees grew near the agency, and several families had trees of their own. The name refers to nuts.

Juglans major   **Walnut**   *Kumcut'ka*

P.B. said that the Box K Ranch and adjacent area in Cataract Canyon was called *kumvicut'kakuwa'a*, "walnuts-grow-there," because of the walnut trees growing in the canyon.

FAMILY LILIACEAE

Allium palmeri   **Wild Onion**   *Haniyooqa'*

This plant was occasionally found in the semi-forested area along the south rim of the Grand Canyon during May and June. M.T. stated that the Havasupai ate wild onions only when very hungry, since they caused headaches. They were baked in a small, unlined pit in the ground, with a fire built on top of the buried onions.

Allium cepa   Cultivated Onion   *Haniyoooa*[1]

Cushing (1882) did not mention cultivated onions in his report. While onions were occasionally cultivated in 1941, they were not as important as among the Hopi and other Pueblo groups.

Calochortus nuttallii   Mariposa or Sego Lily   *Qwakamana*[1]

This plant, which has a bulb like an onion, grew near Grand Canyon Village. In the old days the Havasupai were not supposed to eat deer meat for a month after the deer had eaten this plant. Mariposa was eaten with bread and mescal.

FAMILY AGAVACEAE

Agave utahensis   Mescal, Century Plant   *Viyale*

Century plants grew abundantly along benches of the Grand Canyon and adjacent areas, and occasional plants were found on the desert slopes above and below the village. The collection and preparation of mescal is described in detail in Chapter 3.

Minor uses of the plant included the manufacture of spoons used for thin drinks (S.J.) and of a fiber brush used for the hair and for cleaning grinding stones. To make the brush, the dried matter of a dead and rotten leaf was knocked free from the fibers, which were then bent in two. The upper end of this brush was wrapped with a cord, and the bent portion was covered with buckskin or cloth. The loose fibers were cut to the right length and hardened by burning the ends.

Nolina microcarpa   Beargrass   *'Aqinyuute'*

Beargrass was occasionally found in clumps on the side slopes of canyons and along trails within the canyons. The leaves were woven into a coarse mat upon which mescal was dried. The lower stalk was split open to form an alternative base on which to dry mescal. Leaves were used for thatch. A section of the flower stalk was flattened on both sides and pitted and notched on one side to serve as the hearth of the fire drill (Spier 1928).

Yucca baccata   Soapweed   *Amanat*

This broad-leaved yucca with large, fleshy fruits was abundant in the canyons above the village and on the Plateau.

The leaves contained a good fiber. The terminal spine and a section of the back of the leaf were removed and pounded to free this fiber from the fleshy portion of the leaf. The fiber was often braided into ropes (three- to six-ply) from twelve to thirty feet long that were used for many purposes, including handling horses. The word for braid was *sinavoka* and for a braid of yucca, *amanat-sinaava*.

The Havasupai had uses for many parts of this plant. For example, the terminal spine of yucca served as a needle. A ring of soapweed leaves wrapped in buckskin was used in the hoop-and-pole game. Juice wrung from the leaves which had been heated on the fire was used as a glue to put poison on arrowpoints (Spier 1928). A bundle of yucca fiber was used as a brush with which to apply face paint made of mescal (Spier 1928).

The vegetal material from dried, dead leaves was collected and boiled with pinyon gum. When cool, this hardened mixture was pounded to a powder and then mixed with water to fill in the interstices of baskets which were to hold water. A coat of red paint and then a coat of pinyon gum followed this procedure.

Roots were used as a soap, particularly for washing the hair (E.U.). The roots were peeled, dried, and stored for use. Around the 1850s scalps taken in war were washed in soapweed (Spier 1928).

The fruit, which ripened in September, was prepared for storage in the shape of a mat (see Chapter 3). Fresh fruits were split with the fingers, dried in the sun, and stored in a sack for future use. The fruits were cooked by boiling (E.U., S.J., others). They were considered a sweet food, and Cushing (1882) reported that they were chewed and allowed to ferment to increase their sweetness.

The name is derived from longer forms: *manat-tafsa*, meaning "yucca flowers," and *manat-qwita-qwita*, meaning "points at ends of leaf."

Yucca angustissima   Narrow-leaved Yucca   *'Iny'aava*

This was occasionally found in the village. The leaves were used to tie or repair holes in sacking (E.U., P.B., others). Leaves were also used as tally sticks to keep track of scores in the hidden-ball game. The root and fruits apparently were not used.

FAMILY SALICACEAE

Populus fremontii   Cottonwood   *Ahaa'a*

Cottonwoods were found as occasional trees along the bottoms of the canyons leading toward the village. At the spring just above the village they were abundant. Throughout the lower portion of the Cataract Canyon, cottonwoods were sometimes found in thick stands.

Although the wood was poor, it was virtually the only firewood available close to the village. It was also used for fence posts and in the construction of shades (ramadas) and native-style houses in the canyon. M.M. said that bowls and plates were cut out of cottonwood. Drums were made from hollowed cottonwood logs.

The leafy branches were used to thatch ramadas and houses and were carried in the hand and attached to the neck and biceps of the clown who appeared at dances (Spier 1928).

Cottonwoods provided important, though not preferred, materials for basketry. In the spring the soft, green bark and leaves were stripped from the stems with the fingers. The clean, white stems were then split into three parts and stored in bundles two to three feet long and four to six inches in diameter. Cottonwood, considered inferior to catclaw stems for use in twined basketry, was mainly used in coiled basketry, both for the rods and the binder. Squawberry twigs were the preferred material for coiled basketry, since it did not brown with age like cottonwood.

E.U. said that the unopened cottonwood "berry" was sometimes eaten or chewed like gum. D.I. said that when the cottonwood trees shed white stuff (seeds), it was time to plant; this, he said, occurred late in May and June.

The names of several localities reflected the presence of cottonwoods: Grand View, on the south rim of the Grand Canyon, was called *ahaa'kiyo'o*; a spring in upper Cataract Canyon was known as *ahaakuwa'a'*; a lone cottonwood in Lee Canyon was called *ahaa'thawa'kuwa'a*, and at the head of Matkatamibe Canyon there was *ahaa'kumuhanate* "Cottonwood Knob."

Populus tremuloides   **Aspen**   *Ahaa'cikaava*

This tree was found growing just below the rim of the Grand Canyon and on the highlands north and south of the Grand Canyon (Dodge 1926). The name means "cottonwood-partner."

Salix bonplandiana   **Willow**   *'Iyoo'o'*

A fairly large specimen, with rather broad leaves, was growing in Havasupai Village in 1941. Willow wood was used for fence posts and as fuel for fires. The young shoots were used in basketry in the same way that cottonwood was, but some people considered it inferior to cottonwood.

Salix exigua   Coyote Willow   *Afu'u*

It was common along the riverbank in Cataract Canyon. The young shoots were collected and prepared for use in basketry in the same manner as cottonwood. E.U. said that the stems were split into four, instead of three, parts. P.B. said that tongs for removing cactus fruit were made from the coyote willow.

FAMILY FAGACEAE

Quercus gambelii   Gambel Oak   *Kummpi'i'*

It was found in the yellow-pine areas. The wood was used to make handles for implements, such as hoes and axes (E.U.). The acorns were sometimes eaten in October or November after they fell from the trees (P.B.). M.T. said the acorns were eaten raw or they were parched on a tray. Sometimes they were ground and put into a beef or deer soup a few minutes before it finished cooking, in order to give it flavor.

Quercus turbinella   Scrub Oak   *Tenyiike'*

Scrub oak was found growing in the canyons and on the Plateau at medium altitudes in the pinyon-juniper belt. The wood was used for the handles of hoes (E.U.) and axes (M.M.). The acorns were not eaten (M.M., P.B., others).

FAMILY ULMACEAE

Celtis reticulata   Hackberry   *'Ikwa'a'*

A few trees were seen in the inhabited section of Cataract Canyon. B.B. said hackberry might be used for firewood.

FAMILY MORACEAE

Morus microphylla   Mulberry   *Kapuu'miya'a*

This tree was found in Cataract Canyon, where it was cultivated. There was no definite information as to whether it had been introduced here by the Indians (Dodge 1936). The Walapai name for mulberry was *puim'aa*.

Ficus carica   Fig   *Kwetheqvutaiya*

Fig trees, probably introduced sometime between 1890 and 1910, were mentioned by James (1912). They were not mentioned by Coues (1900) nor by Cushing (1882), both of whom gave fairly extensive lists of crops. Many families obtained their supply of figs through the government agent. The fig trees themselves were obtained from outside sources, or by inheritance. Many fig trees were lost in the 1910 flood.

Several varieties of figs were raised in 1941. They were the first fruits to ripen in the summer. Many of them were eaten fresh, but a considerable number were split open with the fingers, dried in the sun for several days, and stored away in sacks for winter consumption. Both men and women helped in these gathering and drying activities (Mrs. B.J.). Fruit which had fallen to the ground was picked up, ground on the metate, and mixed with water to form a thick paste. The paste was then dried in a six by twelve inch sheet, which was preserved for winter, when it was eaten without cooking (P.B.). The Havasupai name for figs may be broken down into the following: *kwe-* several things are, *theq* leaves, and *vutaiya* big.

FAMILY LORANTHACEAE

Phoradendron juniperinum   Juniper Mistletoe   *'Icoqamuusa*

This plant was pounded and boiled for food (B.B.). The name means "yellow juniper."

FAMILY POLYGONACEAE

Erioqonum corymbosum   Wild Buckwheat   *Ammalkavuhe'e*

This plant was a spiny shrub with yellow or, sometimes, white flowers. P.B., who seems to have been the only informant to see the specimen, said it was used as a medicine. "Take off the leaves and boil them for half an hour. Drink three times a day for a headache." Treatment was repeated the second day if no relief was secured (P.B.). The name translates as "woodrat tail."

Eriogonum inflatum   Desert Trumpet   *Amatkelo'o*

This plant, which grew along the Walapai trail, was characterized by a hollow, inflated stem. D.I. said that in the early spring (April and early May) leafy greens were gathered, boiled from five to ten minutes, and eaten. A child's toy was made from the stem by cutting it off at both ends and using it as a drinking tube (D.I., Mrs. B.J.). According to Mrs. B.J., the name meant "earth dogbane."

Eriogonum racemosum   Wild Buckwheat   *Matahai yaloa'a*

This plant was common in the yellow-pine country. M.T. said the name meant "wind wife."

Eriogonum microthecum   Wild Buckwheat   *'Iwila'thava'mina'mina*

One informant said it was used for tea. Data doubtful. The name comes from the words *'iwila* grass or herb, and *thava* gray.

Rumex crispus   Wild Rhubarb   *Aqlisa*

Rumex crispus was collected in the Havasupai village where it was abundant throughout the inhabited section of the canyon. The rosettes of leaves were cut off the root stalk, rather than pulled from the ground, so that the plant was not killed (E.U.). The leaves were then boiled and eaten.

FAMILY CHENOPODIACEAE

Atriplex canescens   Fourwing Saltbush   *Tasiilka*

The familiar desert saltbush was found growing in many places on the Plateau, as well as in the side canyons, particularly near the village. A handful of leaves in water produces a soapy lather which was rubbed over the body to cure an itch or rash, such as chickenpox or measles. It was also used to wash hair (M.T., Mrs. B.J.). These uses were specifically denied by D.I., P.B. and others. The name of the plant was well known.

Chenopodium spp.   Goosefoot, Pigweed   *Thavakata'uutika*

This was a well-known and important wild food. Spier (1928), who identified it as a pigweed, said that the fruiting heads were collected and allowed to dry for a week and then rubbed between the palms over a tray basket so that the seeds might be winnowed. E.U. said that the entire plant was pulled up and laid on a canvas. If the seeds would not shake out, the fruits were stripped off the stalks with the fingers and then rubbed between the palms to free the seeds. The loose seeds were then placed on a canvas, which was tossed up and down in order that the wind might blow away the chaff. M.T. said that the seeds were knocked directly into a carrying basket, but E.U. thought that the seeds were too small for that method and that the heads were broken off and put on a canvas as described for *iciyace* (see next entry). Both agreed that seeds were rubbed between the palms to free them from the chaff.

The numerous ways of preparing the seeds for food are discussed in detail in Chapter 4. The name is derived from *thava* white, gray and *kata'uutika'* small, round balls.

——— Pigweed *Iciyace*

The identity of *iciyace* remains in doubt, since many informants gave this name to *Atriplex rosea*, an introduced weed. The plant usually referred to by this Havasupai name was found in moist localities on the Plateau. It was a rather nondescript-looking plant, without showy flowers, which grew about three feet high. It may have been a *Chenopodium*, but this identification remains uncertain. The name comes from *ici* many little things, and *yace* seed.

Ceratoides lanata Winterfat *Ahanymmsava*

It was occasionally found on the Plateau, and used mainly for horsefeed. One Havasupai person called it *olomave*, (from *vo'olo'o* horse and *maa'a'* eat). Others called it *ahanymmsava* (from *aha'a* water and *nymmsava* white).

*Salsola kali Russian Thistle, Tumbleweed *'Iwila'atata*

This familiar, introduced tumbleweed was found around the village. The name, which was often applied to other plants, means "plant with stickers." D.I. noted that horses like to eat the young plants.

FAMILY AMARANTHACEAE

Amaranthus hybridus Amaranth *Umkwave*

Although several species occurred in the area, only one was collected. It was found in waste places on the Plateau and in the village, particularly around the gardens.

The leaves of the young plants were picked and cooked like spinach. When the plants were mature (August in the valley, later on the Plateau), the heads were collected in a basket, and dried until the fine black seeds fell out. Spier (1928) and E.U. said the heads were rubbed between the palms. M.M. was probably closer to the facts when she said, "Brush the seeds off with your hand." The seeds, often stored in granaries along with corn (E.U.), were still being used as food in 1941.

FAMILY RANUNCULACEAE

Clematis ligusticifolia   **Clematis**   ' *Iceaqa* ' *cikaava*

This plant was abundant around the spring below the village. The Havasupai had seen this plant many times, but they did not have a fixed name for it, nor did they use it in any way. The name listed here is only one of the many combinations given; it means "grape relative."

Thalictrum fendleri   **Meadowrue**   — — —

Confused with maidenhair fern (*Adiantum capillus-veneris*).

FAMILY BERBERIDACEAE

Berberis fremontii   **Holly Grape**   *Amaqle*

An occasional shrub was found in the pinyon-juniper areas. The yellow root made an excellent yellow dye. A Walapai woman married to a Havasupai decorated baskets with this dye, but the Havasupai used it only as a buckskin dye.

Berberis repens   **Oregon-Grape**   *Kathad* ' *iisma* ' *a*

This low, creeping plant was found along the south rim of the Grand Canyon, especially at Grand View. The roots were used for medicine. P.B. said that the roots were stored until needed, at which time they were boiled for two or three hours. The liquid was allowed to cool and was drunk three times a day for stomach upsets and headache. M.M. said it was good for colds and stomach ailments, acting as a laxative. M.T. said that it was good for a sick baby as well as an adult. For children the root was peeled and boiled, and the resulting liquid was strained and diluted to half strength with water. It was given four times a day before feeding, about a teaspoonful at a time. The adult dose was half a cup. Colds or aches were helped by rubbing the body all over with a rag dipped in the liquid. Coyote was a medicine man, and mythology tells how he used this medicine (B.B.). The name of the plant *kathad* ' *iisma* ' *a* means "coyote medicine."

FAMILY CRUCIFERAE

| *Capsella bursa-pastoris* | Shepherds Purse | *Hamuwale* |

It was found growing in the vicinity of Grand Canyon Village. The Havasupai sometimes confused it with other plants.

| *Descurainia* spp. | Tansy Mustards | *Iqthiva* |

These little plants were common throughout the study area. Several species (*D. obtusa, D. pinnata, D. sophia*) were represented in the collections. These species were not differentiated by the Havasupai. Tansy mustard was a well-known and important source of wild seeds. The seeds, which ripened for the most part early in the spring or summer, were knocked into a carrying basket. As many as two full sacks could be obtained in a day (M.T.). Although the seeds were very small, they were parched on a tray and ground on a grinding stone. See Chapter 4 for the various ways these seeds were prepared as food.

| *Lepidium lasiocarpum* | Peppergrass | *Hamuwale* |

This was a mustard-like plant with round seed pods. Seeds which almost certainly belonged to this genus were obtained from M.M.; yet repeated questioning with specimens of this species and of *L. montanum* resulted in conflicting data. Obviously, one or more species were known by this name. The descriptions of this plant indicated that it ripened in July in the valley and somewhat later on the Plateau. It was prepared in a variety of ways.

| **Rorippa nasturtium-aquaticum* | Watercress | — — — |

Watercress was introduced about 1910 (P.B.), and by 1941 it was growing abundantly in the village along Cataract Creek. The Havasupai were just beginning to eat it in 1941. It had no established native name.

| *Stanleya pinnata* | Desert Plume | *'Isuuta* |

Desert plume grew along the canyon walls, particularly in the vicinity of the village, and was the source of one of the best-known wild foods. The young leaves were collected early in the spring before the flowers appeared. I.U. and E.U. specified that the plant must be cut, for if it was pulled out by the roots it would not grow again.

When desert plume grew in seleniferous soils it developed a poison (Kearney and Peebles 1942). The Havasupai, Hopi, and Navajo all knew that this plant could not be eaten raw (M.T., P.B.). It had to be boiled in water (the water was thrown away), and then either washed or boiled two or three more times before it was safe to eat. I.U. said that if it was cooked outdoors where it was windy it would taste bitter.

| *Thlaspi arvense* | **Pennycress** | *Hamuwalevutaiya* |
| *Thlaspi montanum* | **Wild Candytuft** | *Hamuwalevutaiya* |

Both species were found on the south rim of the Grand Canyon. M.T. said it was used in the same way as peppergrass (*Lepidium*). The name means "large peppergrass."

FAMILY CAPPARIDACEAE

| *Cleome serrulata* | **Rocky Mountain Beeweed** | *Madiika* |

Occasionally found in the canyons of the study area. It was not consistently nor widely recognized among the Havasupai. P.B., M.M., and others thought that the seeds were eaten.

FAMILY SAXIFRAGACEAE

| *Fendlera rupicola* | **Saxifrage** | *I'imowade* |

Occasionally found along the rim of the canyon. The wood was very hard and tough—ideal for arrow foreshafts. Short pieces of saxifrage (a few inches in length) were collected green. The wood was heated in the ashes and straightened. Heating also softened the wood sufficiently so that it could be inserted into the hollow end of the reed arrowshaft (E.U.). It might be necessary to bind it on with sinew (P.B.). The point of this foreshaft was sharpened with a knife or by rubbing on a stone and was resharpened when the point became dull (E.U.).

| *Ribes cereum* | **Currant** | *Hwanyimoval* |

This plant was occasionally found on the Plateau and was not differentiated by the Havasupai from *R. inebrians,* with which it intergrades. The stems, used for wooden arrows (P.B., M.T.), were gathered in November when the wood was hard. A section about two and a half feet long was selected, and feathers were attached to one end. The other end was split and a stone or metal point was inserted and bound into position with deer sinew (P.B.). These arrows were used in war or in hunting large game, such as deer or mountain sheep. The berries were not eaten (P.B., M.T.). The name often given was *'ici- hwanyi-mo-va-le* (*'icihwan-* means "those who feel like fighting").

FAMILY ROSACEAE

Amelanchier utahensis   Serviceberry   *Amovale*

This was a small tree found occasionally on the canyon rim. Possibly other species were to be included under the Havasupai name.

The wood was particularly hard and durable, and was sought after by basket makers for the rims of their carrying baskets (E.U., P.B..) and flat parching trays, and for construction of cradleboards (E.U.). The wood was collected green, heated in hot ashes, and bent and lashed in the desired shape; when it cooled it retained this modified shape (E.U.).

The long, straight stems made good arrows (P.B. and others). The heavy, wooden game arrow was made from a straight stem, about three feet long, cleaned of bark and side branches. Feathers were attached to one end; the other end was split for about an inch, and an arrowhead was inserted and bound in place with deer sinew (P.B.). M.T. said that the spindle of the fire drill might be made of this wood.

Deer were seen eating the serviceberry fruit, but the Havasupai did not eat it (P.B.).

Cercocarpus ledifolius   Mountain-Mahogany   *I'i'ihwata*

This was occasionally on the rocky points along the rims of the Grand Canyon, such as at Grand View Point. Other plant species may have been called by the same name. The red inner bark was made into a buckskin dye (P.B., Mrs. B.J.). When the wood was dry, the bark was removed with a knife, and a pound (or two) was boiled in water for two hours. When it cooled, the liquid was brushed onto the buckskin and worked into the surface with a brush (P.B.). The name means "red wood."

Chamaebatiaria millefolium   Fern Bush   *Hwanyimoval'cikaava*

It was occasionally found on the Plateau. The name means "wild currant-relative."

Coleogyne ramosissima   Blackbush   *Kawila*

This was a low shrub covering large areas on the Tonto Platform in the Grand Canyon. It was widely recognized among the Havasupai as a good feed for stock in the absence of grass.

Cowania mexicana   Cliff-rose   *Cioiyale*

Cliff-rose was found at the higher altitudes of the Plateau, particularly along the rims of the Grand Canyon. It had a fine, soft bark (often confused with that of the juniper) which was used as tinder for the fire drill. It was also crushed and rubbed to make it soft and then stuffed into overshoes to maintain warmth. An infant's cradleboard was often surrounded with a thick layer of this soft bark, and it served as an absorbent diaper for children. Sleeping mats, described in detail by Spier (1928), were made from loosely twisted ropes of this bark (P.B., E.U.).

The green branches were boiled together with other plants, including sagebrush and juniper, and used as a cure for colds. The mixture loosened the mucus and acted as a laxative.

The meaning of the Havasupai name for this plant was "growing with several branches."

Fallugia paradoxa   Apache Plume   *Mataki'i*

It was abundant on the canyon walls and on the Plateau. Apache plume was often used for the top ring of baskets (E.U., Mrs. B.J., M.T.) and for the ladderback rungs of the cradleboards (P.B.).

*Malus sylvestris   Apple   *Aa'pula*

By 1941 apples were frequently raised in the village. They appeared to be of relatively recent introduction, for they were not mentioned in any of the early accounts. The Havasupai name was derived from the English word for this fruit.

*Prunus amygdalus   Almond   *Kwecikaakecetemasei'ya*

E.U. said that his father planted the one tree in the village. The name means "cultivated walnuts."

Prunus armeniaca   Apricot   *Thipalahai'ikuwi'i*

Apricots were not mentioned by Garcés in 1776 but were listed in Cushing's (1882) report and in Coues's (1900) report. The trees were obtained through the Indian Agency or from mail-order houses. The name was from the Havasupai words *thipala* peach and *hai'iku'u* white man.

Prunus persica   Peach   *Thipala*

Although Garcés did not mention peaches in his 1776 diary, they were mentioned by Hodge in 1877. Since the Havasupai name (*thipala*) is derived from the Hopi word (*sipala* peach), it is probable that the Havasupai learned about peaches from the Hopi.

Many of the trees growing in the village in 1941 had been inherited from the previous generations, and new stock was being added from mail-order catalogues. The government agent had been active in helping the Havasupai obtain good peach stock for many years (*Arizona Graphic* 1899). At one time they grew more fruit than they could consume, and considerable amounts were traded to other tribes or sold to neighboring ranchers and miners (James 1912). A great many trees had been lost in the flood of 1910. Little, if any, of the peach crop was sold outside Cataract Canyon in 1941.

Peaches were sometimes eaten green because of the demand for fresh fruit (Spier 1928), although large quantities were split open with the fingers, pitted, and dried in the sun for later consumption. To prepare the dried fruits one pounded them a bit and stewed them in water for half an hour; then the water was drunk (Mrs. B.J.). This method of preparation was observed by Cushing in 1881 (Spier 1928).

Peaches were an important part of the Havasupai diet during the months of July and August. In late August or early September, the annual circle dance and feast was held. This was known in English as the "Peach Dance," though it apparently had no corresponding native term with similar meaning.

Peach trees were personal property even when planted on land belonging to another person. Formerly, when a dead person was cremated, his peach trees were burned or destroyed along with his other personal property.

Several varieties of peaches were recognized by the Havasupai.

The following is a list of those varieties with their native names:

white peach	*thipala-nymmsava*
yellow cling	*thipala-kwatna*
small variety	*thipala-thipida*
nectarine	*thipala-nolawata* ("smooth-peach")

*Prunus domestica   **Plum, Prune**   *Thona'thona'*

A few of these trees had been obtained from outside sources by 1941. The word *thona'-thona'* means "to be wrinkled, dry"; the tree also went by the name *kwe-'inya'-thona'thona'*.

*Prunus spp.   **Cherries**   — — —

The cherries reported by Hoover in 1929 might be of hybrid origin (for example, *P. avium* with *P. cerasus*).

*Pyrus communis   **Pear**   *Lakatova*

A few of these trees had been obtained from Anglo-Americans by 1941. Pear also went by the name *kwelakatova*, which means "large, hooked things."

FAMILY LEGUMINOSAE

Acacia greggii   Catclaw   *Cicasa*

An occasional tree was found growing in the dry canyon bottoms, on the tallus slopes near the village, and in the upper reaches of Cataract Canyon. Catclaw, an important source of strong basketry material, was considered superior for twined basketry. The twigs were stripped of leaves and thorns by running them through the hand, protected by a piece of cloth or canvas. They were roughly sorted and the butt ends trimmed off to lengths of two and three feet. The shorter butts were mashed soft between two stones. The longer twigs, used for warp, were split in three—beginning at the tip—using the teeth and hands. Only the two outside strips were used; the inside one was discarded. The strips were scraped to a uniform thickness by drawing them a few times across a knife. The twigs were collected green in July or August. If stored, they had to be soaked for two or three days before they could be used (Spier 1928).

When the fruits were ripe in the fall they were collected and spread on a blanket. They were then beaten with a stick to free the seeds from the pods. The seeds were collected and half or more of them stored in a skin sack or blanket bag. When the seeds were to be used, they were roasted in a parching tray, ground on a grinding stone and made into bread. M.M. used a brush made of catclaw twigs to brush off metates.

Astragalus spp.	Loco Weed	— — —

Several species of *Astragalus* were found growing in the Havasupai range; some of them were poisonous (Kearney and Peebles 1942). There was no consistent recognition or terminology for this species. Several informants considered the seeds edible.

Cercis occidentalis	Redbud	*Kihala*

A few trees grew near the springs along the canyon trail above the village. Most informants denied that they were used for anything. B.B. said the wood was used for bows. E.U. said handles for tools were made from it and it might be used for fence posts. Considering the limited supply of material, it could not have been an important resource.

Dalea spp.	Indigo Bushes	— — —

Cushing (1882) said that the Havasupai used a blue face paint derived from the root of the wild indigo. Willey (1912) said that they decorated their baskets with this blue paint. The Havasupai may once have obtained native indigo from Mexico, possibly through the Hopi.

Lotus mearnsii	Deer Vetch	*Nyakeskam*

M.T. applied this name to this species. This, or some related form, was apparently used for food. The data were inadequate.

Medicago sativa	Alfalfa	*'Alfa'alfa*

The tendency of the Havasupai language to reduplicate syllables was strongly highlighted in the way they modified the name of this introduced plant. Sometimes the term *iwila*, normally applied to practically any growing plant, was used specifically for alfalfa, which was raised only to a limited extent in the valley.

*Melilotus spp. Sweet Clovers I'i'ka'hali'i

The sweet clovers were introduced plants. The leaves were dried, ground up, placed in a small bundle, and tied onto clothes (women only) for a perfume (M.T.).

Phaseolus acutifolius Tepary Bean — — —

Not distinguished from the kidney bean (*Phaseolus vulgaris*).

*Phaseolus lunatus Lima Bean *Diklaapa'laapa'*

Limas were used much as kidney beans were. The name means "very flat bean."

*Phaseolus vulgaris Kidney Bean *Madiika*

The Havasupai did not have as many varieties of beans as the Hopi. Garcés in 1776 was fed beans (Coues 1900). The Havasupai apparently received seeds from their neighbors in all directions—the Mohave, Walapai, and Hopi.

Beans were often planted in the same fields and at the same time as corn; they also ripened at the same time as corn. Beans were shelled by rubbing them between the hands over a parching tray. The material was placed in a basket and tossed in the air in order to winnow out the debris and leave the heavier beans in the basket. Beans were stored for later use in granaries or in the frame houses.

Like most seeds, beans were parched, ground, and added to hot water to make a soup or mush, called *madiiktava* ground beans. This soup might also contain ground corn. Beans were also cooked with fresh corn cut from the cob. Another way of cooking them was in hot ashes under a fire. In 1941 they were usually boiled.

The following is a list of several varieties of beans distinguished by the Havasupai:

bumpy pink beans	*dika-lalivotava*
Hopi beans	*mooka-madiika*
spotted beans	*dik-inyuda*
pink beans	*madiik-walsaica*
red and white spotted beans	*madiik-walumtava*

*Pisum sativum Pea — — —

A few Havasupai families cultivated peas in 1941.

Prosopis juliflora   Mesquite   *Anaala*

Mesquite was occasionally found in the vicinity of the village,
although there were not sufficient numbers of mesquite trees to provide any great quantity of food. The beans ripened in late September
and October.

The branches were not used in basketry, although the base frame
of the cradleboard was made of mesquite. The wood was used occasionally for firewood, but the supply was very limited. The spindle of
the fire drill was often made of dried mesquite root (Spier (1928).

The mesquite pod was sometimes eaten raw like a stick of candy.
For cooked food usages, see Chapter 4.

*Vigna sinensis   Black Eyed Pea   *Madiika'i'ma'a*

This introduced species was occasionally grown. Because the "eye" of
this bean was likened to the black mask on the eye of the Quail, they
named it "quail bean." Seeds were obtained from M.M.

FAMILY GERANIACEAE

Erodium cicutarium   Filaree   *'Iwila'huuvaka*

This was an introduced plant with sharp, pointed fruit that was said to
look like a mosquito (*huuvaka*); besides, "it sticks you" (M.T., B.B.).

Geranium fremontii   Geranium   *'Iwila'hapak*

M.T. said the Navajo use it for medicine and that it grows by a spring
(*hapak*). This statement opens up questions, since this plant does not
necessarily grow next to springs.

FAMILY ZYGOPHYLLACEAE

Larrea divaricata   Creosote Bush   *'Epil*

This bush, which grows only in the lower deserts, was the habitat of
a lac-producing insect. The lac was formerly an important element in
native trade. Although the Havasupai themselves no longer collected
it in 1941, they obtained it in trade from the Mohave and, in turn,
traded it to the Hopi. A chunk of lac, two or three inches in diameter,
could be traded for a blanket. The Havasupai used lac to attach
arrowpoints (B.B.)

Tribulus terrestris   Caltrop   '*Iwilaqwava*

This was an introduced weed with hard, sharp-pointed fruits. This weed had a number of names: '*iwila*'-*qwava* (from '*iwila* weed and *qwa-* horn); '*iwila*'*atata* (from -*tata* spine); *waksiqwa*'*a* (from *waksi*'*i* cow and *qwa*'*a* horn).

FAMILY RUTACEAE

Ptelea pallida   Hop Tree   '*Aqwakamuuna*

An occasional tree of this species was found in the side canyons. It was used for firewood, though the supply was limited.

The leaves, which had a strong odor, were pounded up together with jimson weed (*Datura*), scorpions, and other noxious items. The mixture was then applied to the tips of arrows for use in hunting large game and in warfare. It was said that even a slight scratch from an arrow so treated would insure death (B.B. and others).

As a medicine, the leaves were boiled in water and the resulting liquid rubbed on a child's abdomen to cure stomachache (D.I.). Mrs. B.J. reported that it was once tried as a medicine in the sweatbath, but that it caused the bather's cheeks to swell and was, therefore, declared a failure. The name means "deer stomach."

Thamnosma montana   Turpentine Broom   '*Ammalkamanuuna*

This was a common, little, bushy plant, with a very strong odor, that was used for medicine. The leaves were pounded and then rubbed onto a hurting abdomen (B.B.). M.M. said that the plant could be soaked in cool water; others (E.U. and others) said that it should be boiled for a few minutes. The resulting liquid was very bitter, but the patient must drink a cupful one to three times during a day. This would cause vomiting (M.M.) or act as a laxative "within two hours" (E.U). The name means "woodrat stomach."

FAMILY ANACARDIACEAE

Rhus trilobata   Squaw Bush   *Katha*'*e*'*e*.

This was a common shrub found along the rims of the Grand Canyon.

The stems were an important basketry material. The best results were obtained by waiting until late fall to collect the current year's growth (E.U. and others). Basketry made of green wood was not strong and was inclined to warp. Only the long, straight stems were collected. They were preferred to cottonwood because they stayed white, whereas cottonwood stems turned brown with age (Mrs. B.J.). Squawbush was also the preferred material for the binder of coiled basketry, and was not infrequently used for the manufacture of twined baskets.

The red berries were collected in July or August in a carrying basket. They were crushed on the grinding stone and allowed to soak in a little water; then they were ground again, and more water was added (M.T. and others). The resulting liquid was used as a drink. Some people preferred to add sugar to the liquid, and the sweetened drink was often referred to as "lemonade." For storage, the berries were dried in the sun and kept in sacks. To prepare the dried berries, a person pounded them up on the grinding stone and soaked them in water for half an hour (E.U. and others). More cold water was then added to make a drink. Ida insisted that the liquid be strained, but this seemed to be an unusual refinement that was not ordinarily practiced. B.B. said he added mescal to sweeten the drink (use of mescal probably preceded the use of sugar).

FAMILY CELASTRACEAE

Canotia holacantha   **False Paloverde**   *'Iqsii'i*

A clump of these small trees, with numerous spinelike, leafless branches, was found growing in the canyon near the village. The Havasupai name was widely known, but the material was not used in any way.

Mortonia scabrella   — — —   *Ahuute*

An occasional plant of this species was found in Cataract Canyon. It was a small shrub with very tough wood and small, white flowers. B.B. and P.B. said that it grew on the Esplanade. It was used to make the wooden foreshaft on the reed arrow, frequently without any additional point.

FAMILY RHAMNACEAE

Rhamnus betulaefolia   Buck Thorn   *I'i'tapal*

Buck thorn was occasionally found along the upper part of the Walapai Trail. It was not consistently recognized by the Havasupai informants.

Ziziphus obtusifolia   Gray Thorn   *I'i'itata*

This thorny bush was found forming dense thickets in the village. The name means "woodspine."

FAMILY VITACEAE

Vitis arizonica   Wild Grape   *'Iceaqa*

This plant was found growing over rocks and shrubs near the springs by the village. The hoop of the hoop-and-pole game was sometimes made from grape vines (D.I.). The fruit was known to be edible.

*Vitis spp.   Cultivated Grapes   *'Iceaqa*

A few families cultivated grape vines.

*Parthenocissus spp.   Virginia-Creepers   *'Iceaqa'cikaava*

This was found growing on the walls and fences beside the government buildings.

FAMILY MALVACEAE

*Gossypium spp.   Cottons   *Hecawa*

The Havasupai occasionally obtained cottonseed from the Hopi so they could raise a few plants for use in the strike-a-light. When the cotton was picked, the seeds were removed and the cotton spread out on a blanket. The cotton was not spun but was twisted into thread with the fingers (M.T.). The thread was braided into a thick cord, *hecawa'sinava* ("cotton, twisted"), which was then threaded into a hollow bone tube made from the femur of a wildcat. The spark from the strike-a-light was caught on the slightly protruding end of the cord. Once the fire was lit, the cord was pulled back into the tube (B.B.). Cotton goods (called *hecawa* in 1941) were obtained from the Hopi in trade.

Sphaeralcea spp.   Globe Mallows   *Cimapuunika*

Several species—including *S. fendleri, S. grossulariaefolia,* and and *S. parvifolia*—were all collected within the Havasupai range. They were not differentiated by the Havasupai. If a person handled one of these plants and then touched his face, itching and even sores resulted (E.I., D.I., M.T., B.B.).

It was said that the juice of the globe mallow was made into a paste which was mixed with clay before it was molded into a pot (S.J.). Juice of this plant appears to have been only one of several ingredients within this paste (Spier 1928).

FAMILY TAMARICACEAE

Tamarix chinensis   Tamarix, Tamarisk, Salt Cedar   — — —

A single specimen of this introduced species had been brought down to the village by 1941.*

FAMILY LOASACEAE

Mentzelia albicaulis   Blazing Star   *Sile'e*

This was a low-growing plant with small yellow flowers. The leaves stuck tenaciously to clothing. It is possible that several species were included under this native name. Formerly a very important food plant, blazing star was found in open glades on the Plateau. A special, basketry beater, *sile'aovuk,* was used to knock the seeds into a small carrying basket held in the left hand. As this basket filled it was dumped over the shoulder into a large burden basket carried on the back (M.T.). The Havasupai name means "sandy."

FAMILY CACTACEAE

Echinocereus spp.   Hedgehog Cacti   *Matahaiya'imaa'a*

The name means "wind testicles."

Echinocactus spp.   Barrel Cacti   *Emultate*

This name was probably applied to several species that were described as big, tall, barrel cacti growing on the Plateau. Pieces of

---

* Richard Hevly (personal communication) has pointed out that by 1985 this species was firmly established in the Havasupai area and throughout the lower Grand Canyon.

the plant were used as a tray for baked mescal. The spines were burned off and the body of the cactus was cut into slices with an axe. These were spread out on the ground and the cooked mescal was placed on top of them (E.U).

A cooking vessel, *multatkwetalomia,* was sometimes improvised from these large cacti. This practice occurred particularly on hunting expeditions, though it might also have occasionally been done at home.

The spines on some of these cacti were quite wide and red. These were removed, warmed at the fire, and bent into finger rings (B.B., P.B.). Cushing (1882) saw numerous finger rings of bright red cactus thorns worn in great numbers by the women. He also mentioned earrings of beaded cactus thorns (Cushing 1882).

The seeds, which were ripe in July, were used either fresh or dried. They were parched and ground to make mush (Mrs. B.J.). The name means "sometimes spine."

Opuntia phaeacantha   Prickly Pear   *Alava*

The Havasupai term included several species, which were found in Cataract Canyon and at lower portions of the Plateau.

The body of the cactus was used as a target in archery practice (Spier 1928).

The fruit, called *hate' e,* ripened in August and September, and was removed from the plant with tongs made of *Salix exigua* (P.B.). To remove the fine spines, the fruits were rolled on the ground and brushed with a handful of Mormon tea or any other weed which was handy (P.B.). They were finally rubbed with a rag (Spier 1928) and placed in a burden basket to be carried home to camp. In camp, they were either eaten fresh or split in half and, after the seeds were removed, allowed to dry in the sun for a day (P.B., Mrs. B.J., and others). The dried fruit might be pounded into a cake for storage; pieces of this cake were eaten directly without further preparation (Mrs. B.J). Prickly pear fruit was one of the few sweet foods eaten before the coming of commercial sugar. Unlike mescal, this fruit was not used as seasoning with other foods (Mrs. B.J.).

Alava was mentioned by S.J. as one of the plants used in preparing pottery clay.

Tatooing was accomplished by pricking the design into the skin with cactus spines moistened and dipped into ground charcoal. P.B.

said spines of this cactus were best, since they were the sharpest ones that could be found.

Opuntia spp.   **Chollas**   *Taqwiise*

This name applied to any cholla cactus, although it typically referred to a large form, with branches resembling deer horns. The Havasupai recognized the spines of these cacti as being unusually difficult to remove (P.B., E.U., B.B.). This was due to a thin sheath that covered the spine and remained in the flesh after the spine itself had been removed. The cholla was one of the plants from which the liquid was used to mix with pottery clay (S.J., B.B.). B.B. said this liquid was boiled.

An area in which this plant was found growing, the upper section of Cataract Canyon, was known as *taqwiisqliyanya* (P.B.).

———   ———   *Kwatha'vuwaka*

Descriptions of this plant indicate that it was either a short, stocky cholla (*Opuntia* spp.) or some form of an elongated barrel cactus. M.T. said it was about a foot tall, as big as her forearm, and had red flowers. Descriptions of this kind were not found to be particularly accurate. M.M. said it was small, like a barrel cactus, in contrast to the prickly pear.

M.M. described how it was used in pottery making. The spines were burned off and the "skin" peeled away. The sticky interior was then rubbed over the molded, but unfired, pot. M.T., however, said to break the cactus open, cut the inside into small pieces, put these into water, and work (squeeze) them with the fingers. This liquid was rubbed all over the pot. The first part of the name derives from *akwatha* "yellow."

FAMILY ELAEAGNACEAE

Shepherdia rotundifolia   **Buffalo Berry**   ———

The plant was occasionally found near the head of the Grand Canyon trail leading from the south rim to the village.

Informants did not consistently name this shrub, though they all seemed to recognize it. When the plant was hit or otherwise disturbed, a cloud of the fine dust rose from the underside of the leaves. If this dust got into the eyes it was said to make the eyes sore and to even cause blindness (M.T., B.B., P.B., M.M. and others).

FAMILY UMBELLIFERAE

Apium graveolens   **Celery**   ———

The familiar Old World celery was introduced and by 1941 was found growing wild below the village. The Havasupai had no name for it and apparently did not eat it or use it in any way.

FAMILY CORNACEAE

Garrya spp.   **Silk-tassels**   *Taltale*

This large evergreen shrub was occasionally found on the Plateau. P.B. said that whistles were made from the straight, thick stocks. There was a feeling that disturbing this plant would bring rain.

Fraxinus anomala   **Singleleaf Ash**   ———

Specimens of this species were not consistently recognized, though it was found growing in Cataract Canyon near the village and along the trails.

Fraxinus pennsylvanica   **Velvet Ash**   *Kapu'u*

This plant grew in the vicinity of the village. The wood was used for handles of various tools—such as hoes or axes (B.B., E.U.)—for fuel, and for house and fence construction (B.B., E.U., Mrs. B.J., M.M.). The hoop for the hoop-and-pole game and the oval frame for the cradleboard might also be made of this wood. Tongs, *sataav*, for handling hot or prickly objects were made from a green branch of this plant: the branch was flattened on one side, notched in the middle, and then bent double and bound until it was dry (Spier 1928).

It was best known among the Havasupai as the material from which bows were made (B.B., E.U., P.B., D.I. and others). A young tree was selected and its branches trimmed close so that the plant would grow straight. After two or three years, the tree was cut (E.U., and Spier 1928). No information could be obtained from the informants as to ownership of these trees, though the supply was obviously limited.

A spring near the village was named *kapu'kiyo'o* because of a group of these trees which grew nearby. The Havasupai name can be broken down to the following: probably from *ka-hapu'u*, (*ka* he who has and *hapu'u* bow).

FAMILY GENTIANACEAE

Swertia radiata   **Deers Ears**   *Hatakwila'iisma'a'*

It was a tall plant that grew in the pine country. It had large deep roots with medicinal properties. Before it could be dug, the Havasupai had to make a speech to the plant telling it what a good medicine it was and that help was needed. The entire root was boiled for five minutes and the resulting liquid cooled by adding cold water. A drink of this was taken in the morning and again before going to bed at night as a remedy for digestive upsets, colds, and similar troubles. It might be given by a medicine man. When taken in conjunction with a sweat bath, it was good for gonorrhea. The medicine was said to have been used originally by Wolf, hence it was Wolf's medicine. The name is from *hatakwila* wolf and *iisma'a* medicine.

FAMILY APOCYNACEAE

Apocynum medium   **Dogbane, Indian-Hemp**   *Kelo'o*

This species was collected near the village and on the rim of Cataract Canyon.

The stems, collected in winter when the plant was dry and the leaves had fallen, were pounded to loosen the bark. The bark was not broken down but used as a unit: strips were braided and worn as a belt, which might be prepared as needed in the field (Mrs. B.J.). Some informants denied this usage (E.U., B.B., P.B. and others) or attributed it to the Mohave (M.T.).

The green stem exudes a white, milky substance when broken. E.U. said that when he was young, children would try to get this "milk" on their playmates' faces; if successfully applied, it made the victim's eyelids stick together.

The stems were also used occasionally for thatch on the houses (P.B., Mrs. B.J., E.U., M.T., D.I. and others).

FAMILY ASCLEPIADACEAE

Sarcostemma cynanchoides   **Climbing Milkweed**   — — —

An occasional climbing vine was found growing near the village. Children removed the leaves and twisted the stocks into a rope used in play (P.B. and others).

FAMILY CONVOLVULACEAE

Convolvulus arvensis   **Bindweed**   — — —

An introduced weed occasionally seen on the Plateau. It was recognized but not named (P.B., E.U., M.T.).

Cuscuta campestris   **Dodder**   *Sahamaca*

This twining, parasitic plant was occasionally seen in the village, particularly on alfalfa.

*Ipomoea batatas   **Sweet Potato**   *Paapamiyula*

Sweet potatoes were a crop which by 1941 had been introduced with some success. A plot under the direct supervision of the Indian Sub-agent served the dual purpose of providing potatoes for the school and demonstrating the method of their cultivation to the residents of the village. The name recorded here was given by D.I., but it may not have had wide acceptance. It was a literal translation of the English word "potato" (*paapa*) and the Spanish word for "sweet" (*miyula*).

Ipomoea coccinea   **Scarlet Morning Glory**   — — —

The scarlet flowers of this plant, which belongs to the same genus as the morning glory, were narrowly trumpet shaped. The vine was occasionally found near the village and was recognized by some informants, but not named.

FAMILY POLEMONIACEAE

Gilia sinuata   **Gilia**   *'Iwila'kaiya*

This inconspicuous plant was found growing on the Plateau. The seeds were collected, parched on a tray, and ground. After being dampened with a little water, the ground seeds were worked with the hands into the consistency of peanut butter. According to M.B. and B.B., sometimes this substance would be mixed with *sile'e* (*Mentzelia*). Information on this species was not completely satisfactory. The Havasupai name probably included *G.tenuiflora*, which was also found in this area.

Ipomopsis aggregata   **Sky Rocket**   *'Iluwi'ci'uuta*

This bright, red-flowered plant was abundant on the Plateau.

It was recognized as being different from two other similar forms, Indian Paint Brush (*Castellija* spp.) and scarlet bugler (Red-flowered

Pentstemon spp.), which were given the same native name and were avoided in the same manner. When specimens were offered to children in his presence, one man prevented the children from handling it. In the Havasupai name, *'iluwi'i* means "rattlesnake," and *ci'uuta* means "downy feather."

Phlox spp.   **Phlox**   *Smakatu'u*

Specimens of two forms, *P. austromontana* and *P. longifolia*, were collected on the South Rim near Grand Canyon Village, though plants also occur elsewhere within the Havasupai range. M.B. and her daughter said that phlox was used as medicine for stomachache (the daughter was giving it to her baby at the time). The root was pounded on a rock, boiled for five or ten minutes, and the liquid was allowed to cool. An average dose was half a cup. For colds or aches, the liquid might also be rubbed over all the body, in the same fashion as Oregon-grape (*Berberis repens*), which had the same Havasupai name. Part of the name, *smaka*, means "to sleep."

FAMILY VERBENACEAE

Aloysia wrightii   **Wright Lippa**   — — —

This occasionally found shrub with aromatic foliage was observed in Cataract Canyon, above the village, and was used for tea (Mrs. B.J., M.T., B.B. and others). A handful of leaves was put into boiling water and allowed to boil for a minute. This drink was preferred to Mormon tea as a substitute for commercial tea or coffee. Spier (1928) said that it was boiled and taken copiously for slight distempers, rheumatism, and headaches.

FAMILY LABIATAE

*Marrubium vulgare   **Hoarhound**   — — —

This introduced herb was common near the village. Many of the informants recognized it, but there was no established name for it.

Salvia davidsonii   **Sage**   *'Iluwi'ci'uuta*

This plant was rare but could be found on talus slopes in the village. It was not differentiated from *Penstemon barbatus*, which it resembled (B.B.).

FAMILY SOLONACEAE

| *Capsicum annuum* | Chili Pepper | — — — |

Listed by James (1903) as one of the Havasupai crops. It was not being grown in 1941.

| *Datura meteloides* | Jimson Weed | *Smadikatu'u'* |

This plant, which had gray leaves and large, lily-like flowers, was found near the village.

A few leaves or a couple of seeds, if eaten, would make a person intoxicated for a day or more (Spier 1928, E.U., P.B., D.I., B.B. and others). When a person ate jimson weed, his throat would become dry and the victim would do strange things, such as hoeing up corn or bumping into objects (E.U.). The person under this influence had dreams, such as being in a crowd of people who play and dance, or being in the company of a girl who disappears when you grab her (E.U.). The older people strongly opposed use of jimson weed, although the tales told about it were enough to make any adventurous young man want to try it once.

Datura was listed by Spier (1928) as one ingredient of arrow poison. The plant could also be used medicinally: a leaf was roughly folded several times and rubbed on the surface of the skin where a person had been bitten by a red ant (D.I., E.U.).

The pronunciation of the Havasupai name was very fast; the English meaning is "it caused ringing in the ears," or "deaf."

| *Lycium pallidum* | Desert Thorn | *'Iyace* |

This stiff, spiny shrub with red berries was occasionally found on the Plateau and in the canyon. The berries were gathered in a carrying basket and then spread on a blanket to dry in the sun. Once dry, they were ground and put into water to make a drink (M.T., B.B.). The Havasupai name and usage probably included *L. andersonii*, a similar species found in the canyon. The name means "wood seeds."

| *Lycopersicon esculentum* | Tomato | — — — |

Although this plant had no native name, it was being cultivated in 1941.

Nicotiana attenuata　　　　Wild Tobacco　　　　*'U'uuva*

This species of tobacco was found growing on the Plateau and in Cataract Canyon in areas which had been cleared of other vegetation. It was to be looked for near tanks and water holes and in areas which had been burned over (B.B., E.U.). Apparently, if there was no tobacco available under normal conditions, fires were set and tobacco seed distributed in the ashes by the Indians themselves (Spier 1928). This species was smoked by the Havasupai for pleasure; there was no indication that it was used ceremonially.

Nicotiana trigonophylla　　　Coyote Tobacco　　　*Kathadnyi'uuva*

This species of tobacco was common along the talus slopes near the village and in places on the Plateau. Apparently, this plant, too, was smoked in aboriginal times, though the preceding species was preferred. This variety, known as Coyote's tobacco, was said to have been what resulted when Coyote tried to make regular tobacco. Spier (1928) says this was the variety which Coyote grew for his own use. B.B. said Coyote tried to smoke this.

Solanum douglasii　　　　　Nightshade　　　　　— — —

This climbing vine, found near the village, was recognized but not named. The berries were too bitter to be eaten (M.M., P.B., E.U., D.I., B.B.).

FAMILY SCROPHULARIACEAE

Castilleja integra	Paint Brush	*'Iluwi'ci'uuta*
Mimulus cardinalis	Crimson Monkey Flower	*'Iluwi'ci'uuta*
Penstemon barbatus	Beardtongue	*'Iluwi'ci'uuta*
Penstemon eatoni	Beardtongue	*'Iluwi'ci'uuta*

These several species, together with *Ipomopsis aggregata* and *Salvia davidsonii*, all have bright red flowers and were all known by the same Havasupai name.

When Rattlesnake was a man, he wore a downy red feather in his hair, which is now represented by these flowers. The flowers should not be handled, especially by children, lest Snake bite them.

The name can be broken down to the following: *'iluwi'i*, meaning "rattlesnake," and *ci'uuta*, meaning "downy feather."

Penstemon palmeri   Beardtongue   *'Iwilaka'o'o*

This plant had a large, showy, pink flower and was found along the Walapai trail. The name presented here was given by only one informant, D.I.

Penstemon pachyphyllus   Blue Beardtongue   *'Iyaasmaa'a*

This blue-flowered species was occasionally found on the Plateau. M.T. said that a deer hunter would often fold the leaf lengthwise and place it in his mouth with the folded edge out. By sharply drawing his breath in, the hunter could produce a sound like that of a baby deer. The name was given only by M.T., and she did not repeat the name when the same species was seen later. The name means "turkey eat."

FAMILY BIGNONIACEAE

Chilopsis linearis   Desert Willow   *Ci'mova*

Large stands of this shrub were found growing along the river above the village. The smaller branches were collected in the spring or summer. The bark was removed and the unsplit wood was used as rod foundations in coil basketry (P.B., E.U., I.U., and others). P.B. said the wood was too brittle to be used for the binding.

FAMILY MARTYNIACEAE

Proboscidea parviflora   Devil's Claw   *Halaaka*

Two varieties of devil's claw occurred in the canyon. One, which had short spines and black seeds, was found growing wild in the fields and waste places near the village. Specimens of this plant were identified as *P. parviflora*. This form might have been cultivated, though it was usually collected from plants seeding themselves in the vicinity of the fields. The seedlings were recognized and were often allowed to grow in the gardens where other plants would be weeded out (D.I.).

The second variety had longer spines on the pod and white seeds. This second variety was usually planted by the women at the same time as corn, but harvested only when the fields had dried out (E.U.). The fruits were removed and dried in the sun. Seeds were edible and were sometimes eaten. The spines were broken off near the base and stored for future use, most often as decorative elements in basketry.

The origin of this cultivated type has been debated. Spier (1928) attributed it to a Walapai woman who married a Havasupai and then obtained it from her sister, who had obtained it from the Paiute. E.U. remembered that this woman planted a field of devil's claw and sold a superior product. Mrs. B.J. claimed to have introduced this form from the Mohave herself. B.B. thought that it had been obtained long ago from the Hopi. E.U. suggested the Yavapai. All these explanations were possibilities.*

The long-spined form was known as *halaakakiyula* (*kiyula* long), while the short-spined form was known as *halaakata'uutika* (*kata'uutika* ball).

FAMILY OROBANCHACEAE

Orobanche spp.   **Broomrapes**   *'Ama'ula'maa'a*

M.T. applied this name to three different plants all collected on the Plateau: *O. cooperi*, *O. fasciculata*, and *O. multiflora arenosa*. B.B. did not recognize *O. multiflora arenosa*. The Havasupai name means "antelope eat."

FAMILY PLANTAGINACEAE

Plantago purshii   **Indian Wheat**   *Thavakata'uutika*

P.B. said that in July the seeds of this abundant but inconspicuous little weed were knocked into a basket with a stick. They were then ground and made into mush. Other informants gave a variety of similar names but denied the use (D.I., B.B., M.M., E.U., and others). The name means "white balls."

*Plantago major   **Common Plantain**   — — —

This introduced species resembled the important food species *Rumex* (Spier 1928). There was no Havasupai name for this species.

FAMILY CAPRIFOLIACEAE

Sambucus glauca   **Elder**   *Taltale*

This name also applied, perhaps erroneously, to *Garrya flavescens*. It was said that flutes were made of *taltale*, but M.T., viewing the plant, said that whistles were not made of this material but of *temeya'a* and *qlisakepal*, both unidentified plants.

---

* For further discussion on this subject, see Nabhan et al. (1981) and Bretting (1982).

Symphoricarpos spp.   Snowberries   ʼ*Iwila*ʼ*hataka*

This low shrub was found in the higher portions of the Plateau near Grand Canyon. The stems were used to make the rim of the shade for the cradleboard (M. T., P. B.). The name which applied to this species also applied to *Bouteloua* spp.

FAMILY CUCURBITACEAE

Citrullus vulgaris   Watermelon   *Suumaca*

The Havasupai had grown watermelons for many years prior to 1941. The records were not clear, because reference was often made to "all kinds of melons," but James (1903) specifically mentioned them around the turn of the century. Carefully selected seeds were stored in cloth bundles in little, stone storage chambers under the cliffs (Spier 1928). Seeds which were not wanted for future planting were parched and ground to make *sumkwin* and other dishes (S. J.). Several of the varieties recognized by the Havasupai were:

white seeded	*suumacanymmsava*
black seeded	*suumaca inyaca*
striped surface	*suumaca* ʼ *inua*

Cucumis melo   Melons, Muskmelons, Cantaloupe   *Meloona* ʼ

Melons were mentioned by most observers, beginning with an account in *The Miner* (1880). Some of these reports may refer to watermelons, although it is unclear which melons they actually meant. The Havasupai name was derived from the English "melon" or the Spanish "*melón*," perhaps as a result of contact with the Hopi, who used a similar term (Whiting 1939). Cushing (1882) said that in 1881 melons were dried for storage and were stewed when wanted for food. This practice was similar to the Hopi usage.

Cucurbita foetidissima   Buffalo Gourd   ʼ*Inmaa* ʼ*a*

This plant was occasionally found in waste places in the inhabited portion of Cataract Canyon.

Girls were experts at juggling the ball-like fruits (M. M.); boys played with the fruit, but as a rule they did not juggle (Spier 1928).

A wooden ball, made from the root of this plant, was used in playing the "four hills" game. Spier (1928) gave an excellent description of this game. He said that the ball was cut from yucca root, but this may be an error, as several informants insisted that the root was from this wild gourd (D.I., E.U., M.M., and others). The ball, called *kata'uutika* (D.I.), was not painted (E.U.).

*Cucurbita moschata   Squash, Pumpkin   *Hmte'e*

Two types of squash were no longer common in 1941: the earlier type was apparently the striped cushaw, a large heavy squash with a crook neck and light, vertical stripes on the body; a similar squash with a round body was also described as being an old type. Two other types were not seen growing at all in 1941: one of these was said to have a woody texture and, hence, was called *hmtei'i*; another was said to be gray or cream colored and was called *hmte'thavakita'uutika*.

Other types were known and raised. Squash was planted four to five inches deep, with four seeds to a hole (Spier 1928), in the same fields with corn. The corn often ripened and dried up prior to the ripening of the squash and pumpkins (E.U.). Seeds not wanted for future planting were dried, parched, shelled, and eaten. They were sometimes ground to form a paste or mixed with corn in a mush (M.M.). See Chapter 4 for further discussion of preparation and use as food.

A four- to five-inch hole was cut in the top of the squash, and the shell was carefully hollowed out and dried in the sun. These squash- or pumpkin-shell vessels were filled with seeds, beans, etc., and hidden where enemy raiders could not find them (S.J., M.M.). Seeds were carefully selected for the following year's crop and stored away in cloth sacks (Spier 1928) or in these shell containers.

Squash vines were attacked by a worm about half an inch long called *hmte'kitepuuya* (*Euschistus*, stink bug).

*Lagenaria vulgaris   Gourd   *'Ih'nale*

These gourds should not be confused with the little, wild gourds (*Cucurbita foetidissima*) or pumpkins described above. The Havasupai appear to have been dependent upon the Hopi for their supply of gourds or, at least, of gourd seeds. In 1941 only one or two medicine men raised them, and they had obtained the seeds from the Hopi.

Rattles were often made from this gourd. Unlike Hopi rattles, Havasupai rattles were punctured with small holes in particular patterns. Spier (1928) said that only shamans knew the significance of these patterns, but that they were not the star patterns used by Navajo. The rattling elements were stones (D.I. and others). The rattles had a wooden handle which protruded through the far side of the gourd, with the inner surface resting upon a collar. A thong wound around the protruding portion of the shaft kept the gourd from slipping off.

Large, hourglass-shaped gourds were formerly used for carrying water on foot or on horseback trips away from home (E.U.). Spier (1928) said that, when walking, a man would carry such a container bound to the middle of his back. The container was held in place by a rope tied around the man's waist and the constricted portion of the gourd. Larger-bodied forms were infrequently used as water storage vessels. The end of the elongated neck was cut off square and had a stopper made of grass, crushed cedarbark, corncob, or the cutoff portion of the gourd itself (Spier 1928).

FAMILY COMPOSITAE

Artemisia curuthii   Wormwood, Sagebrush   '*Inyanyipa*'*cikaava*

This was occasionally found on the Plateau. M.T. said the name meant "relative of cousin."

Artemisia ludoviciana   Wormwood, Sagebrush   '*Iwila*'*thava*'*mina*'*mina*

This was found growing in the vicinity of the village. Sprays of this shrub were used in the sweatbath, where it served as a substitute for *A. tridentata*. It was said to have beneficial effects in case of sickness (M.T., P.B.), and P.B. said it could be used like tea. For tea, a handful of leaves was boiled for ten or fifteen minutes in a coffeepot. Spier (1928) said that a ring of this species was put around a person's limb to draw out the poison of a snake bite. This plant's name also applies to *Eriogonum microthecum*.

Artemisia pacifica   Wormwood, Sagebrush   '*Inyanyipa*'*a*

Plants of this species were occasionally found on the Plateau. M.T. described collecting seeds of this plant and of *A. carruthii*. She said to take off the top of the stalk and rub the seeds between the hands over a carrying basket. In this way half a sack of seeds might be collected. The plants were hard to find; nevertheless, they were used extensively in the old days. After the seeds were prepared by parching, they were ground, moistened with a little water, and worked into a sticky dough, which was eaten with mescal.

The name can be broken down into three Havasupai words: *'inyaa'a* sun, *-nyi-* his, and *apa'a* arrow.

Artemisia tridentata   Sagebrush   *'Imoqwapata*

This plant, an evergreen shrub, could be found in large stands over much of the Plateau. It was used frequently as medicine, particularly for a runny nose, cough, or intestinal upset. There was considerable variation in this use. Leafy stems were placed on the fire (coals), and the resulting fumes were inhaled for a cold or runny nose (E.U.). The fresh leaves were chewed for a cough (E.U. and others). More often, it was pounded a bit, boiled in water for ten to fifteen minutes (M.M.) or twenty minutes (I.U.), and then cooled and drunk. The usual dose, a cupful, was taken before breakfast and again after supper. This treatment was continued until the cold was gone, usually in two or three days (I.U.). Another method was to take two tablespoonfuls every half hour for one day (M.M.). This method was good for a cold (I.U., M.M., M.T., P.B., E.U.), cough (B.B.), sore throat (M.T.), or stomachache. The liquid was also used as a wash for sores or pimples (M.T.).

The shrub was often used for fuel (Spier 1928). The bark was used as a plug to keep water from spilling out of a water jug (E.U.). This plant was the most abundant material available for thatch on the Plateau.

Baccharis emoryi   Groundsel Tree   *Hatavilhiseiiya*

This tall, willow-like bush formed dense stands along the river and was important in controlling erosion. This was probably the tree Cushing (1882) had in mind when he called the Havasupai "the nation of the willows." The male and female flowers were borne on separate plants, which were not differentiated by the Havasupai.

Aside from its use in brush house construction, firewood, and fence posts, it was of little use to the Havasupai, though it was sometimes used in coil basketry (I.U., Mrs. B.J. and others), and E.U. said it was the best wood for making planting sticks.

When the seeds were shed, they covered the neighboring ground with a thick layer of "down." Children set this "down" on fire, producing a sudden burst of flame which spread rapidly over a considerable area. The elders disapproved of this action because of the fire hazard (E.U.).

E.U. also described a "peashooter" made by removing the pith from a large section of stem and inserting a piston made from a smaller twig of the same bush. This, he said, was sufficiently powerful to kill birds and to hurt, but not seriously injure, a human.

A point about midway between Beaver Falls and the mouth of Cataract Creek on the west bank was called *hatavilhewaiya* because these shrubs grew there. The name was usually abbreviated to *hatavil*, but sometimes it was given as '*iwilaseiya* or *hiseiya*.

Chrysothamnus nauseosus	Rabbit Brush	'*Iwila*'*akwatha*

This species, abundant on the Plateau south of the Grand Canyon, was said to flower when the constellation "Hand" rose (ca. August). The name, which means "yellow plant," was sometimes applied to other yellow flowers.

Cirsium spp.	Thistles	'*Ethi*'*itahe*'

Several species of thistles were found growing in the Havasupai area, including *Cirsium neomexicanum* and *C. nidulum*. When food was scarce, hunting parties would pick the leaves, hold them in the flames of a fire until the spines were burned off, and eat them (M.T., P.B.).

Gaillardia pinnatifida	Blanket Flower	'*Immetale*

This plant was abundant along the South Rim of the Grand Canyon. M.T., who gave the above name, said the seeds were knocked into a carrying basket, roasted, ground, and worked into an edible spread resembling peanut butter. Other informants failed to recognize the plant (B.B., D.I., E.U.).

Gutierrezia sarothrae	Snakeweed	*Ko*'*hwaiyo*'*o*

This plant was abundant on the open stretches of the Plateau below the yellow pines area. A myth tells how Rabbit Man, in trying to escape Sun's wrath, crawled under this bush. The top of the bush was burned by Sun's heat, but not the lower portion. Rabbit escaped with only a slight scorch on the back of his neck, which all rabbits retain to the present (P.B., E.U.).

Helianthus petiolaris   Wild Sunflower   'Ikata

This plant was found growing wild in waste places on the Plateau. The seeds were thinner, though longer in gross length, than the cultivated form: hence they were sometimes called *katekiyula* (*kiyula* long). They were used in the same way as the cultivated species. M. T. said that the shells were not removed from the wild seeds.

Helianthus annuus   Common Sunflower   'Ikata

This cultivated form had shorter, but heavier, seeds, which were purplish black in color, in contrast to the black and white striped seeds of the wild form. The cultivated seeds were obtained from the Hopi. The Havasupai seeds showed a mixture of wild and cultivated forms, indicating less care in selection of seeds.

Seeds were planted in the gardens with or near the corn. When the heads were ripe, they were cut from the stocks and dried in the sun. When dry, they were placed on an old canvas and beaten with sticks to remove the seeds. (E. U., P. B.). The seeds, in turn, were dried in the sun (P. B.), and a considerable quantity was stored away for winter use (E. U.). The seeds for the next year's crop were selected for sweetness, dried, bundled in a cloth and set aside for spring planting (Spier 1928). Refer to Chapter 4 for information about cooking these seeds.

Cushing (1882) mentioned that oil extracted from sunflower seeds was sometimes mixed with red face paint.

Leucelene ericoides   White Aster   *Smakumtuteva*

This small, white aster was found along the South Rim near Grand Canyon Village. It was used as a medicine for digestive troubles. Some said to boil the whole plant and drink the resulting tea twice a day until cured. Others, however, said to use the roots only. These were pounded and boiled, and the resulting liquid was drunk. This liquid was also rubbed over the stomach. This was not a strong medicine and might be given to young children and babies, as well as adults. Both M. T. and her daughter applied this name and described this usage for the white aster (three instances) and also for *Phlox* spp. (two instances). P. B. gave essentially the same usage, with some modifications: the roots, which could be stored, were boiled for half an hour. P. B.'s dosage was half a cup taken three times a day before meals, for one day. (Note that P. B. undoubtedly had three meals a day, while M.T. and her daughter probably still conformed to the older pattern of two meals a day.) P.B. also used a different name, 'ammalakamanuuna, which he also applied to *Thamnosma montana*.

Pectis angustifolia   Lemon-scented Marigold   'Iwila'saha

This plant was collected near the eastern end of the Grand Canyon. It was used by the Hopi and possibly the Havasupai for food and flavoring (Spier 1928). The name means "plant smells."

Pectis papposa   Chinchweed   'Ammalka'thuca

This plant was found growing frequently in the sandy soil above the village. P.B. said that the name means "woodrat feces" ('ammalka woodrat, *thuca* feces). He also said that this plant was formerly picked fresh, dipped in salted water, and eaten with mush or corn-meal as a condiment. This description essentially matched the Hopi usage. No mention of this use and only conflicting names were obtained from Mrs. B.J., M.M., E.U., and others. P.B.'s family may well have learned about the use of this plant from the Hopi. The terminology was highly questionable.

Porophyllum gracile   Odora   'Umthulmaa'a

This was a highly scented herb growing on the talus slopes near the village. It was well known as a medicine that was prepared by pounding and placing it in water. It was frequently boiled. The result-ing liquid was used as a wash on a sore or rubbed in as a liniment. The crushed herb itself was often rubbed on the skin "so that the smell will go in." The liquid was drunk, though this practice was less common. The medicine was used primarily against pain or aches, including abdominal pain (Mrs. B.J., M.M., D.I., B.B. and others). The words within this plant's Havasupai name mean "chuckwalla eat."

Tessaria sericea   Arrowweed   Matemu'u

This shrub, which was abundant near the village, was easily confused at first glance with saltbush. It was widely used for thatch in building houses in the canyon (Mrs. B.J., E.U., P.B., and others). Spier (1928) referred to it as "white willow" and said it was the preferred material.

Straight stems were used to form the back of the cradleboard (E.U., P.B., and others). The stems were also used to make arrows (Mrs. B.J., M.M.), especially for children (P.B. and others); these were the wooden, not reed, arrows. Sticks used to peg a hide to the ground when it was being stretched during tanning were made from this bush (E.U.).

Spier (1928) said that the leaves were chewed to relieve irritation in the throat.

Verbesina encelioides   Crown Beard   *Yokatava*

This was found growing in waste areas on the Plateau. The name means "toothache" (*yo'o* tooth), though the reason for this could not be learned. It was not used for a toothache or for anything else (E.U. and others). This name was also applied to a wide variety of other yellow, daisy-like flowers.

Xanthium strumarium   Cocklebur   *Thulkumthe'e*

This was an occasional weed found on the Plateau. It was a constant nuisance on the trail, for the spiny fruits got into the horses' tails and had to be cut out (E.U., B.B. D.I., and others).

Xylorhiza tortifolia   Desert Aster   *'I'i'ka'hali'i*

This plant, with a large, purple (fading to white), daisy-like flower, was found near the Walapai Hilltop and in the vicinity of the village. B.B. said it was used by both men and women as a perfume to counteract body odors. The leaves were ground up and carried in the clothes.

UNIDENTIFIED PLANTS

———   ———   *'Inyapita*

This was described as having small, white flowers in the very early spring. The leaves were boiled with corn meal to make mush (M.T.). It was said that if the plant bloomed out of season in December, a big snow storm would come. E.U. said, "I saw the flowers in December one year. I told Grandfather. He just had to go and see for himself. He said we would have a big snow, and by the 26th of December, we did." Apparently, it grew only on the Plateau. The name was given to a sterile specimen of *Antennaria* (M.T.) and to *Townsendia* (P.B.). Other informants gave different names to these species; there was no agreement and much confusion. It would appear to have been a low, leafy plant, similar to these two species.

———   ———   *Cimuwaiya'cikaava*

This plant was described as similar in appearance to Mormon tea (*cimowaiya*), but gray in color. P.B. said it had small, purple flowers like alfalfa. It was said to grow in a few places on the Esplanade. Like Mormon tea, it was used for medicine. A bundle of twigs was boiled for about an hour and the resulting liquid was allowed to cool. Half a cup of the dark brown liquid was drunk in the morning and again at night. If the bowels had not moved by morning it was taken again. It was also taken in case of stomach pains (P.B., E.U.).

———   ———   *Pakwiyoiya*

This plant, which grew on the Plateau, had an odor resembling the turpentine broom (*Thamnosma montana*). E.U. said that if it was worn by a man as a perfume, it would attract women.

———   ———   *Matko'udoo'o*

The leaves were eaten without cooking, in March when the plant came up. The flowers were white. B.B. and S.J. said it grew on the Red Wall area above the village. The name referred to a plant which probably resembled *Thlaspi*, though perhaps with a trailing habit, like *Allionia*. There was some suggestion that the root was eaten, rather than the leaves.

Havasupai
Informants

A. F. Whiting's information about the Havasupai — including their knowledge and uses of animals, plants, minerals, metals, rocks, and stars — came primarily from nine informants. The following is a coded list and brief description of those Indians. Initials (not necessarily the real ones) have been used instead of full names to protect the privacy of the individuals and families involved. Additional data are available to scholarly researchers. For further information, contact Dr. P. David Seaman; Department of Anthropology; Northern Arizona University; Flagstaff, Arizona 86001.

B.B. He was P.B.'s father, and he lived at the Village in Cataract Canyon. An older man, he was loved by children and patient with ethnographers. His English was fair.

D.I. A middle-aged man who lived at the Village in Cataract Canyon, D.I. was a sympathetic informant with good knowledge of Havasupai life. His English was fair.

E.U. He was a middle-aged man who lived at Grand Canyon Village, where he was frequently employed on the railroad. He had not lived in the native village since he went away to school. E.U.'s extensive knowledge of the old Havasupai life was acquired from his grandfather, a Havasupai leader who raised him. E.U. was a good informant who spoke fair English.

I.U. E.U.'s wife.

M.M. A woman of infinite patience, who was a good basket-maker and an excellent informant, M.M. was the daughter of a Havasupai leader. Her son and daughter-in-law translated.

Mrs. B.J. She was a garrulous, old woman with good knowledge of the old ways. Various translators were used at her home in Cataract Canyon.

M.T. She was one of the oldest Havasupai women of those interviewed. Because she was poor, even by Havasupai standards, she retained many of the old ways of life. M.T. was said to be the last Havasupai woman to collect seeds on the Plateau. Her daughter acted as translator.

P.B. P.B., who was older than E.U., was occasionally employed at the Grand Canyon. His family was the last to maintain winter camps on the Plateau. P.B. had a wide knowledge of basic Havasupai life. His English was fair.

S.J. She was one of the oldest Havasupai women living in 1941. She remembered Apache raids, how to manufacture pottery, and many other elements of the old lifestyle. In 1941 S.J. lived at the Village in Cataract Canyon; by 1950 she had moved to Desert View, at the rim of the Grand Canyon. Since S.J. spoke no English, a translator was used.

Bibliography

Akwasasne Notes
1973a   Environmentalists resist return of Havasupai lands. 5(4):15.
1973b   Havasupai people bring their fight to Washington. 5(6):21.
1975   Havasupai Grand Canyon lands returned. 7(1):36.
Allstrom, Erik W.
1938   Three thousand feet down. *Indians at Work* 6(1):37–38.
Alvarado, Anita L.
1970   Cultural determinants of population stability in the Havasupai Indians. *American Journal of Physical Anthropology* 33(1):9–14.
American Ornithologists' Union
1983   *Check-list of North American birds.* 6th edition. Baltimore.
Arizona Commission of Indian Affairs
1960a   *Hualapai Report.* Report No. 1. Phoenix.
1960b   *Report on Havasupai Reservation, Yavapai-Prescott Reservation, Camp Verde Yavapai-Apache Reservation.* Report No. 2. Phoenix.
1964a   *Survey of the Hualapai Reservation.* Phoenix.
1964b   *Survey of the Havasupai Reservation.* Phoenix.
Arizona Graphic
1899   *The Yava-Supai Indians.* October 7, pages 2–3. Phoenix, Arizona.

This is intended as a definitive bibliography for the Havasupai. It includes items from Whiting's original *Havasupai Habitat* manuscripts, items found in Whiting's notes after his death, and numerous other entries of more recent date. Any missing item is an unintentional oversight. The editors would appreciate hearing about omissions and other errors.

Arizona Republic
  1983   State case on Indians set back. June 15, 94(30):B-7.
Arizona Writers Project
  1940   The Havasupai. In *The Havasupai and the Hualapai.* Arizona
          State Teachers College, *Bulletin* 21(5):5–18.
Association of American Indian Affairs
  1975?   The Havasupai: prisoners of the Grand Canyon. New York.
          [Undated manuscript has references through 1974.]
Bacon, Diane
  1974   The Havasupai. *Quarterly of the Southwestern Association on
          Indian Affairs* 9(3):10–11.
Bamerlin, John
  1973   Post Office: Arizona style. *Arizona Highways* 49(5):10–15.
Bartlett, Katharine
  1936   Hopi history. No. 2. Museum of Northern Arizona, Flag-
          staff, *Museum Notes* 8:33–37.
  1981   Alfred F. Whiting, 1912–1978. *Journal of Ethnobiology*
          1(1):1–5.
The Basket
  1903   The Havasupai Indians and their homes. 1(3):20–33.
Bateman, Paul C.
  1972   *Culture change and revival in Pai basketry.* M.A. thesis, North-
          ern Arizona University, Flagstaff.
Beale, E. F.
  1858   *Wagon Road from Fort Defiance to the Colorado River.* House
          Ex. Doc. 124, 35th Cong., 1st Sess. Government Printing
          Office, Washington, D.C.
Berry, Stillman S.
  1946   A shell necklace from the Havasupai Indians. *Plateau* 19(2):
          29–30.
Biggs, Bruce
  1957   Testing intelligibility among Yuman languages. *International
          Journal of American Linguistics* 23:57–62.
Bleisch, Michael John
  1977   Land of the blue water people. *Desert Magazine* 40(5):16–19.
Borror, Donald J. and Dwight M. DeLong
  1971   *An introduction to the study of insects.* 3rd edition. Holt,
          Rinehart and Winston, New York.
Breed, Jack
  1948a   Land of the Havasupai. *National Geographic Magazine* 93:
          655–674.
  1948b   Ride a horse to Havasupai. *Arizona Highways* 24(7):12–21.
  1955   The Havasupai. In *Indians of the Americas,* pages 409–411.
          National Geographic Society, Washington, D.C.
Breed, William J., George Billingsley, and Scott Imsland
  1975   A preliminary survey of the ground water of the Havasupai

reservation, Coconino County, Flagstaff, Arizona. Unpublished manuscript. Department of Geology, Museum of Northern Arizona, Flagstaff.

Bretting, P. K.
1982   Morphological differentiation of *Proboscidea parviflora* ssp. *Parviflora* (Martyniaceae) under domestication. *American Journal of Botany* 69(10):1531–1537.

Bunzel, Ruth
1932   Zuni kachinas. Bureau of American Ethnology, *47th Annual Report*, pages 837–1086. Government Printing Office, Washington, D.C.

Cadman, Charles W.
1932?   Letter to E. D. McKee. In files of Grand Canyon Natural History Association, Grand Canyon, Arizona.

Casanova, Frank E.
1962   Trails to Supai in Cataract Canyon. *Plateau* 39(3):124–129.
1968   General Crook visits the Supais: as reported by John G. Banke. *Arizona and the West* 10(3):253–276.

Chemi, James M.
1963   Carrying the mail to Supai. *Arizona Highways* 39(7):40–43.

Cole, Ben
1974   Sen. Humphrey supports Havasupais. *Qua'toqti* 1(50):4.

Colton, Harold S.
1940   Tracing the lost mines of the padres. *Plateau* 13(2):17–22.
1943   What can we do about lac? *Plateau* 15(3):46–48.
1945   The *patayan* problem in the Colorado River valley. *Southwestern Journal of Anthropology* 1:114–121.

Commissioner of Indian Affairs
1884   *Annual Report.* House Ex. Doc. 1, Pt. 5, 48th Cong., 2nd Sess., Gov. Printing Office, Washington, D.C.
1893   *Annual Report.* House Ex. Doc. 14, Pt. 1, 53rd Cong., 2nd Sess., Gov. Printing Office, Washington, D.C.
1895   *Annual Report.* House Ex. Doc. 5, 54th Cong., 1st Sess., Gov. Printing Office, Washington, D.C.
1902   *Annual Report of the Department of the Interior for the Fiscal Year Ended June 30, 1902.* Pt. 1. Gov. Printing Office, Washington, D.C.

Coues, Elliot (ed.)
1900   *On the trail of a Spanish pioneer: the diary and itinerary of Francisco Garcés in his travels through Sonora, Arizona, and California 1775–1776.* 2 vols. Francis P. Harper, New York. [Volume 2, pages 335–408, deals with the Havasupai.]

Crook, Rena; Leanne Hinton; Edith Putesoy; and Nancy Stenson
1976   Havasupai-English dictionary. Unpublished manuscript.

Crook, Rena; Leanne Hinton, and Nancy Stenson
1977   Literacy and linguistics: the Havasupai writing system. In *Proceedings of the 1976 Hokan-Yuman Languages Workshop,*

Crook, Rena, Leanne Hinton, and Nancy Stenson (*continued*)
James E. Redden, ed. Southern Illinois University, Carbondale, *University Museum Studies*, 11:1–16.

Curtis, Edward S.
1908   *The North American Indian.* Vol. 2. The Plimpton Press, Norwood, Massachusetts. [Twenty volumes were published between 1907 and 1930; volume 2, pages 95–102, deals with the Havasupai.]

Cushing, Frank Hamilton
1882   The nation of the willows. *Atlantic Monthly* 50 (September and October):362–374, 541–559.

Davies, Bruce
1973   Tribes oppose Grand Canyon enlargement. *Navajo Times* 14(29), July 26, page A-9.

Deaver, Chester F., and Horace S. Haskell
1955   Ferns and flowering plants of Havasu Canyon. *Plateau* 28: 11–23.

Dellenbaugh, F. S.
1934   Indian red paint. *Masterkey* 8(3):85.

Dobyns, Henry F.
1974   *Prehistoric Indian occupation within the eastern area of the Yuman complex.* Garland Publishing, New York.

Dobyns, Henry F., and Robert C. Euler
1960   A brief history of the northeastern Pai. *Plateau* 32(3):49–57.
1967   *The ghost dance of 1889 among the Pai Indians of northwestern Arizona.* Prescott College Press, Prescott, Arizona.
1970   *Wauba Yuma's people: the comparative socio-political structure of the Pai Indians of Arizona.* Prescott College Press, Prescott, Arizona.
1971   *The Havasupai people.* Indian Tribal Series, Phoenix, Arizona.
1974   Aboriginal socio-political structure and ethnic group concept of the Pai of northwestern Arizona. In *Havasupai Indians*, Robert A. Manners, ed., pages 177–274. Garland Publishing, New York.
1976   *The Walapai people.* Indian Tribal Series, Phoenix, Arizona.

Dobyns, Henry F., and Robert C. Euler (eds.)
1961   The origin of the Pai tribes, by Henry P. Ewing. *Kiva* 26(3): 8–23.

Dodge, Natt
1936   *Trees of Grand Canyon National Park.* Grand Canyon Natural History Association, *Natural History Bulletin* 3.
1949   *Poisonous Dwellers of the Desert.* Southwestern Monuments Association, Santa Fe, New Mexico, *Popular Series* 3.

Doheny, E. L.
1924   *Doheny scientific expedition to the Havasupai Canyon, Northern Arizona.* Oakland Museum, Oakland, California.

Dorsey, George A.
1903   *Indians of the Southwest.* Atchison, Topeka, and Santa Fe Railway System, Chicago.

Douglas, F. H. (compiler)
1931   The Havasupai Indians. Denver Art Museum, Department of Indian Art, Leaflet #33.

Drake, Gordon V.
1955   A history of the Hualapai Indians and a study of the acculturation of Hualapai Indian students. M.A. thesis, Arizona State College, Flagstaff.

Ducheneaux, Karen
1973a   Supais attack environmentalists. *Qua'toqti* 1(20), November 29:7.
1973b   Supais have one more chance to get their land returned. *Qua'toqti* 1(21), December 6:5.

Emerick, Richard
1954a   Recent observations on some aspects of Havasupai culture. M.A. thesis, University of Pennsylvania, Philadelphia.
1954b   The Havasupais, people of Cataract Canyon. University of Pennsylvania, Philadelphia, *University Museum Bulletin* 18(3):33–47.

Essig, Edward Oliver
1926   *Insects of western North America.* Macmillan Company, New York.

Euler, Robert C.
1957   A Cohonina burial. *Plateau* 29:59–62.
1967   The canyon dwellers. *American West* 4(2):22–27, 67–71.
1973   *Havasupai of Arizona, 1150–1890.* Clearwater Publishing Company, New York.
1974a   Havasupai historical data. In *Havasupai Indians,* Robert A. Manners, ed., pages 275–307. Garland Publishing, New York.
1974b   The Pai: cultural conservatives in environmental diversity. In *Collected papers in honor of Florence Hawley Ellis,* R. Frisbie, ed. *Papers of the Archaeological Society of New Mexico* 2:80–87.
1979   The Havasupai of Grand Canyon. *American West* 16(3): 12–18.
1980a   Grand Canyon Indians. In *The Grand Canyon: up close and personal.* Western Montana College Foundation, Dillon.
1980b   People of the blue-green water. *Cobblestone* 1(6):16–31.
1981   Havasupai-Cohonina relationships in Grand Canyon. In *Collected papers in honor of Erik Kellerman Reed,* Albert H. Schroeder, ed., pages 167–176. Albuquerque Archaeological Society Press, *Papers of the Archaeological Society of New Mexico* 6.

Euler, Robert C. (continued)
1982 Ceramic patterns of the Hakataya tradition. In *Southwestern ceramics: a comparative review*, Albert H. Schroeder, ed., pages 52–69. Arizona Archaeological Society, Phoenix, *The Arizona Archaeologist* 15.

Euler, Robert C., and Henry F. Dobyns
1958 Tizon Brown Ware: a descriptive revision. In *Pottery types of the Southwest*. Museum of Northern Arizona, Flagstaff, *Ceramic Series* 3-D.
1961 Ethnic group land rights in the modern state: three case studies. *Human Organization* 20(4):203–207.
1983 Ethnoarchaeology of Pai milling stones. In *Collected papers in honor of Charlie R. Steen, Jr.*, Nancy L. Fox, ed. *Papers of the Archaeological Society of New Mexico* 8:253–267.

Euler, Robert C., and Henry F. Dobyns (eds.)
1960 The Pai tribes, by Henry P. Ewing. *Ethnohistory* 7(1):61–80.
1961 A note on the Pai tribes, by Henry P. Ewing. *Ethnohistory* 8(1):103–104.

Euler, Robert C., and Dee F. Green
1978 An archaeological reconnaissance of Middle Havasu Canyon, Arizona. U.S. Forest Service, Southwestern Region, Albuquerque, *Cultural Resources Report* 22.

Euler, Robert C., and Volney H. Jones
1956 Hermetic sealing as a technique of food preservation among the Indians of the American Southwest. *Proceedings of the American Philosophical Society* 100:87–99.

Ewing, see Dobyns and Euler (eds.), 1961; Euler and Dobyns (eds.), 1960, 1961.

Farrish, Thomas Edwin
1916 *History of Arizona*. Vol. 4. State of Arizona, Phoenix.

Ferry, Phillip
1950 Canyon utopia. *Natural History* 59(2):72–79.

Fewkes, J. Walter
1898 Archaeological expedition to Arizona in 1895. Bureau of American Ethnology, Washington, *Annual Report* 17: 519–744.
1899 Hopi basket dances. *Journal of American Folklore* 12:81–96.

Forde, C. Daryll
1931 Ethnography of the Yuma Indians. *University of California publications in American archaeology and ethnology* 28:83–278.

Franse, Harry G.
1891? Ghost dance in Arizona. *Mohave Miner*. Quoted in *Inter-Ocean* June 25, 1891. Reprinted in *Journal of American Folklore* 5(1892):65–67.
1937 Gwetva. *Arizona Magazine* 1(2):21.
1938a Land of the blue-green water. *Arizona Highways* 14(5):10–11.
1938b Vest pocket horses. *Arizona Highways* 14(10):18–19.

Garcés, Father Francisco. *See* Coues, Elliott. ed.
Goodfriend, Martin
  1967 A follow-up report, Supai, Arizona. Unpublished paper, February 1, 1967. Cited in Zaphiris (1968).
  1976 *The Havasupai Indian reservation: an economic profile.* Privately printed. Santa Monica, California.
Goodwin, Grenville
  1942 *The social organization of the Western Apache.* University of Chicago Press, Chicago.
Griffin, John I.
  1972 *Today with the Havasupai Indians.* Indian Tribal Series, Phoenix, Arizona.
Griffith, Elizabeth
  1963 Adventures in Havasu. *Arizona Highways* 39(7):9–39.
Hall, E. Raymond
  1981 *The mammals of North America.* 2nd edition, 2 volumes. John Wiley and Sons, New York.
Hall, James H. Jr.
  1947 *Report on Havasupai linguistics.* Unpublished manuscript.
Hall, Sharlot M.
  1907 The Indians of Arizona. *Out West* 27(6):471–497.
Halpern, A. M.
  1946 Yuma. *International Journal of American Linguistics* 12:25–33, 147–151, 202–212.
  1947 Yuma (continued). *International Journal of American Linguistics* 13:18–30, 92–107, 147–166.
Hanna, Dan, and Leanne Hinton
  1971 Havasupai medicine song. *Alcheringa* 2:68–75.
Havasupai Tribal Council
  1957 *Law and order code for the Havasupai tribe adopted by ordinance no. 1.* Supai, Arizona.
  1966 *Ten-year overall economic and human resource development plan for the Havasupai tribe, Supai, Arizona.* Supai, Arizona.
Hawbecker, Albert C.
  1936 *Check list of plants of the Grand Canyon National Park.* Grand Canyon Natural History Association, *Natural History Bulletin 6.*
Hayden, Carl (ed.)
  1936 *Walapai papers.* Senate Document No. 273, 75th Cong., 2nd Sess. Government Printing Office, Washington, D.C.
Heald, Weldon F.
  1951 People of the blue-green water. *Travel* 96(6):7–9.
Henderson, Earl Y.
  1928 *The Havasupai Indian Agency, Arizona.* Haskell Printing Department, Lawrence, Kansas.
  1931 *The Havasupai Indian Agency, Arizona.* Office of Indian Affairs, Lawrence, Kansas.

Hinton, Leanne
 1973   The old lady's song: a poetic analysis. *Linguistic Notes from
        LaJolla* 5:19–35.
 1977   *Havasupai songs: a linguistic perspective.* Ph.D. dissertation,
        University of California, San Diego.
Hinton, Richard J.
 1878   *Handbook to Arizona: its resources, history, towns, mines, ruins,
        and scenery.* Payot, Upham and Company, San Francisco.
Hirst, Stephen
 1976   *Life in a narrow place.* David McKay Company, New York.
Hodge, Hiram C.
 1877   *Arizona as it is: the coming country.* Hurd and Houghton, New
        York.
Holabird, W. H.
 1890   Article in *Arizona Enterprise,* August 30.
Hooper, Mildred, and C. R. Hooper
 1976   Land of the blue-water people. *Outdoor Arizona* 48(6):
        28–31.
Hoover, J. W.
 1928   Modern canyon dwellers. *Arizona* 1(5):7–9, 36–38.
 1929   Modern canyon dwellers of Arizona. *Journal of Geography*
        28(Oct):269–278.
Hough, Walter
 1898   Environmental interrelations in Arizona. *American Anthro-
        pologist* 11 (old series): 133–155.
Hualapai Times
 1976   Hualapai bilingual program moves into high gear. 1(1):9.
Hughes, J. Donald
 1977   Havasupai traditions. *Southwest Folklore* 1(2):35–52.
Hymes, Dell H., and William E. Bittle (eds.)
 1967   *Studies in southwestern ethnolinguistics: meaning and history in
        the languages of the American Southwest.* Mouton Publishers,
        The Hague.
Iliff, Flora Gregg
 1954   *People of the blue water: my adventures among the Walapai and
        Havasupai Indians.* Harper Brothers, New York.
Indian Rights Association
 1902   *Nineteenth Annual Report of the Executive Committee of the
        Indian Rights Association for the Year Ending December 6, 1901,*
        pp. 21–29.
Indian Truth
 1951   Havasupai assume responsibility. 28(3):2–3.
James, George Wharton
 1900   *In and around the Grand Canyon.* Little, Brown and Com-
        pany, Boston.
 1903a *Indian basketry and how to make Indian and other baskets.*
        George Wharton James, Pasadena.

1903b   *Indians of the Painted Desert region.* Little, Brown and Company, Boston.
1912   *The Grand Canyon of Arizona: how to see it.* Little, Brown and Company, Boston.
Janson, Donald
1966   People of the blue-green waters. *Audubon* 68(6):464–469.
Joel, Judith
1964   Classification of the Yuman languages. In *Studies in California Linguistics,* William Bright, ed. *University of California Publications in Linguistics* 34:99–105.
1966   *Paipai phonology and morphology.* Ph.D. dissertation, University of California, Los Angeles.
1976   Some notes on Paipai object order and object marking. In *Proceedings of the first Yuman languages workshop,* James E. Redden, ed. Southern Illinois University, Carbondale, *University Museum Studies* 7:142–148.
Johnson, David S., and James M. Hewitt
1977   *An Archaeological assessment of cultural resources within the Havasupai Indian reservation addition.* Office of Arid Land Studies, University of Arizona, Tucson.
Jones, J. Knox Jr., Dilford C. Carter, and Hugh H. Genoways
1973   *Checklist of North American mammals north of Mexico.* Museum of Texas Tech University, *Occasional Papers* 12.
Kearney, Thomas H., and Robert H. Peebles
1942   *Flowering plants and ferns of Arizona.* U.S. Department of Agriculture, Miscellaneous Publications No. 423. Government Printing Office, Washington, D.C.
Keesing, Felix M.
1941   *The South Seas in the modern world.* John Day Company, New York.
Kendall, Martha B.
1975   A preliminary survey of Upland Yuman dialects. *Anthropological Linguistics* 17(3):89–101.
Kitner, Ester H.
1939   Legend of the Havasupais. *Arizona Highways* 15:4–5, 42.
Kozakis, John T.
1967   Program memorandum Truxton Canyon Agency. U.S. Department of the Interior, Bureau of Indian Affairs, Area Office, Phoenix.
Kozlowski, Edwin
1972   *Havasupai simple sentences.* Ph.D. dissertation, Indiana University, Bloomington.
1976a   Remarks on Havasupai phonology. *International Journal of American Linguistics* 42:140–149.
1976b   Havasupai comparatives. In *Proceedings of the first Yuman languages workshop,* James E. Redden, ed. Southern Illinois University, Carbondale, *University Museum Studies* 7:93–97.

Kozlowski, Edwina (*continued*)
    1977   Personal communications to A. F. Whiting regarding Whiting's Havasupai phonology notes, which had been lent to Kozlowski prior to publication of Kozlowski's 1976 articles.
Kroeber, A. L.
    1943   Classification of the Yuman languages. *University of California publications in linguistics* 1(3);21–40.
Kroeber, A. L., ed.
    1935   Walapai ethnography. *Memoirs of the American Anthropological Association* 42.
Langdon, Margaret, and Shirley Silver (eds.)
    1976   *Hokan studies: papers from the first conference on Hokan languages, held in San Diego, California, April 23–25, 1970.* Mouton Publishers, The Hague.
Langley, Dama
    1945   Supai Shangri-La. *Desert Magazine* 9(1):9–12.
Lehr, J. Harry
    1978   *A catalogue of the flora of Arizona.* Desert Botanical Garden, Phoenix.
Lehr, J. Harry, and Donald J. Pinkava
    1980   A catalogue of the flora of Arizona, supplement I. *Journal of the Arizona-Nevada Academy of Science* 15(1):17–32.
    1982   A catalogue of the flora of Arizona, supplement II. *Journal of the Arizona-Nevada Academy of Science* 17(1):19–26.
Little, James A. (ed.)
    1881   *Jacob Hamblin, a narrative of his personal experience, as a frontiersman, missionary to the Indians, and explorer.* 5th Book of the Faith Promoting Series. Juvenile Instruction Office, Salt Lake City, Utah.
Lowe, Charles H. (ed.)
    1964   *The vertebrates of Arizona.* Univ. of Arizona Press, Tucson.
Madden, Ross
    1945   Indian Arcadia in the Southwest. *Travel* 84(5):22–24, 32.
Manners, Robert A.
    1974   Havasupai Indians: an ethnohistorical report. In *Havasupai Indians*, Robert A. Manners, ed, pages 23–175. Garland Publishing, New York.
Manners, Robert A. (ed.)
    1974   *Havasupai Indians.* Garland Publishing, New York.
Marks, Royal D.
    1963   Arguments before the Indian Claims Commission, on behalf of the Havasupai Tribe of the Havasupai Reservation, Arizona. Attorney of record for above petitioner in Docket 91, vs. Navajo Tribe, Docket 229.
Martin, John F.
    1966   *Continuity and change in Havasupai social and economic organization.* Ph.D. dissertation, University of Chicago.

1968   A reconsideration of Havasupai land tenure. *Ethnology* 7(4):450–460.

1973   The organization of land and labor in a marginal economy. *Human Organization* 32(2):153–161.

Mason, Otis Tufton
1904   Aboriginal American basketry. *Annual report of the United States National Museum, 1902.* Government Printing Office, Washington, D.C.

McCowan, S. M.
1899   Article on the Havasupai. In *Report of the Governor of Arizona to the Secretary of the Interior, 1899.* Government Printing Office, Washington, D.C.

McGregor, John C.
1935   Upsetting the balance of nature. Museum of Northern Arizona, Flagstaff, *Museum Notes* 7:45–48.

1951   *The Cohonina culture of northwestern Arizona.* University of Illinois Press, Urbana.

McKee, Barbara; Edwin McKee, and Joyce Herold
1975   *Havasupai baskets and their makers, 1930–1940.* Northland Press, Flagstaff, Arizona.

McKee, Edwin D.
1935   Letter to J. K. Stacy, regarding the Havasupai. March 19. In files of Grand Canyon Natural History Association, Grand Canyon, Arizona.

1941   Personal communication, relating to mining claims in the Havasupai area.

Mearns, Edgar Alexander
1907   *Mammals of the Mexican boundary of the United States.* Smithsonian Institution, United States National Museum, *Bulletin 56.*

Miller, Gerrit S. Jr., and Remington Kellog
1955   *List of North American recent mammals.* Smithsonian Institution, United States National Museum, *Bulletin 205.*

The Miner
1880   A Leadville in Arizona, Jan. 23, p. 2. Prescott, Arizona.

Montandon, George
1923   Gravures et peintures rupestres des Indians du Cataract Canyon (Arizona). *L'Anthropologie* 33:347–355.

1927   Une descente chez les Havazoupaï du Cataract Canyon. Société des américanistes de Paris, *Journal,* n.s., 19:145–154.

Muench, Josef
1940   Home of the blue-green water people. *Natural History* 45:220–223.

Murdock, George P.
1961–   Havasupai. In *Human relations area files,* Section NT14,
1968   Plateau Yumans; available on two microfiche cards. Original files are at the University of Pennsylvania, Philadelphia.

Nabhan, Gary; Alfred F. Whiting; Henry F. Dobyns; Richard M. Hevly; and Robert C. Euler
1981   Devil's claw domestication: evidence from southwestern Indian fields. *Journal of Ethnobiology* 1(1):135–165.

Navajo Times
1967   Government agencies improve Supai area. 8(8), February 23, page 23.

Neibling, Harold E.
1940   Visiting an Indian Eden Deep in an Arizona Canyon. *Kansas City Star,* September 29.

Nelson, Edward W.
1918   Smaller mammals of North America. *National Geographic Magazine* 33:371–493.

Parker, Rupert
1968   Hualapai dam support asked. *Indian Historian* 1(2):15–16.

Paya, Oscar
1973   Havasupai ask support to regain tribal land. *Wassaja* 1(8).

Peterson, Roger Tory
1961   *A field guide to western birds.* 2nd edition, Houghton Mifflin Company, Boston.

Price, William Redwood
1869   Report. November 25. Quoted in Tucker (1938), page 211.

Redden, James E.
1965   *Walapai phonology and morphology.* Ph.D. dissertation, Indiana University, Bloomington.
1966a   Walapai I: phonology. *International Journal of American Linguistics 32:1–16.*
1966b   Walapai II: morphology. *International Journal of American Linguistics* 32:141–163.
1976a   Notes on Walapai syntax. In *Proceedings of the first Yuman languages workshop,* James E. Redden, ed. Southern Illinois University, Carbondale, *University Museum Studies* 7:134–141.
1976b   Walapai syntax: a preliminary statement. In *Hokan Studies,* Margaret Langdon and Shirley Silver, eds., pages 103–112. Mouton Publishers, The Hague.
1977   Notes on Walapai verb root structure. In *Proceedings of the 1976 Hokan-Yuman languages workshop,* James E. Redden, ed. Southern Illinois University, Carbondale, *University of Museum Studies* 11:29–33.

Redden, James E. (ed.)
1976   *Proceedings of the first Yuman languages workshop.* Southern Illinois University, Carbondale, *University Museum Studies* 7.
1977   *Proceedings of the 1976 Hokan-Yuman language workshop.* Southern Illinois University, Carbondale, *University Museum Studies* 11.

1978   *Proceedings of the 1977 Hokan-Yuman languages workshop.* Southern Illinois University, Carbondale, *Occasional Papers on Linguistics* 2.

1979   *Proceedings of the 1978 Hokan languages workshop.* Southern Illinois University, Carbondale, *Occasional Papers on Linguistics* 5.

1980   *Proceedings of the 1979 Hokan languages workshop.* Southern Illinois University, Carbondale, *Occasional Papers on Linguistics* 7.

1981   *Proceedings of the 1980 Hokan languages workshop.* Southern Illinois University, Carbondale, *Occasional Papers on Linguistics* 9.

Reed, Allen C.
1949   Peach festival in Supailand. *Arizona Highways* 25(7):8–13.

Reilly, P. T.
1970   The disappearing Havasupai corn-planting ceremony. *Masterkey* 44(1):30–34.

Rhodes, Willard (recorder and annotator)
1951   Walapai funeral song and Havasupai stick game song. In *Music of the American Indians of the Southwest.* Ethnic Folkways Library, New York.

Rigby, Elizabeth
1958   Primitive village in Havasupai Canyon. *Desert Magazine* 21(1):13–14.

Sapir, Edward
1917   The position of Yana in the Hokan stock. *University of California Publication in American Archaeology and Ethnology* 13:1–34.

Schroeder, Albert H.
1953   A brief history of the Havasupai. *Plateau* 25(3):45–52.

Schwartz, Douglas W.
1956   The Havasupai 600 A.D.–1955 A.D.: a short cultural history. *Plateau* 28:77–85.

1957   Climate change and culture history in the Grand Canyon region. *American Antiquity* 22:372–377.

1958   Prehistoric man in the Grand Canyon. *Scientific American* 198(2):97–100, 102.

1959   Culture area and time depth: the four worlds of the Havasupai. *American Anthropologist* 61(6):1060–1070.

1967   *Havasupai prehistory: thirteen centuries of cultural development.* Ph.D. dissertation, Yale University.

Schwartz, Douglas W., and Milton Wetherill
1957   A Cohonina cremation. *Plateau* 29:63–65.

Scoyen, E. T.
1951   Were there giants in those days? *Arizona Highways* 27(7): 36–39.

Seiden, William
    1963   *Morphology and phonology of Havasupai.* Ph.D. dissertation,
            Indiana University, Bloomington.
Selvin, Joseph R.
    1928   The amphibians of western North America. *Occasional
            Papers of the California Academy of Science* 16.
Service, Elman
    1947   Recent observations on Havasupai land tenure. *Southwestern
            Journal of Anthropology* 3:360–366.
Shufeldt, R. W.
    1891   Some observations on the Havasu-pai Indians. *Proceedings
            of U.S. National Museum* 14(859):387–390.
Sitgreaves, L.
    1853   *Report of an expedition down the Zuni and Colorado rivers.*
            Senate Ex. Doc. 59, 32nd Cong., 2nd Sess. Gov. Printing
            Office, Washington, D.C.
Smith, Catherine Chambliss
    1946   Havasupai. *Arizona Highways* 22(8):10–16.
Smith, Charline G.
    1970   *Culture and diabetes among the Upland Yuman Indians.* Ph.D.
            dissertation, University of Utah, Salt Lake City.
Smith, Dama Margaret
    1923   Home of a doomed tribe. *Good Housekeeping Magazine* (Sep-
            tember 1923), pages 38–39, 196–198, 201–202, 205.
Smith, Hobart M.
    1946   *Handbook of lizards.* Comstock Publishing Company, Ithaca,
            New York.
Smithson, Carma Lee
    1959   *The Havasupai woman.* University of Utah Press, Salt Lake
            City.
Smithson, Carma Lee, and Robert C. Euler
    1964   *Havasupai religion and mythology.* University of Utah Press,
            Salt Lake City.
Spier, Leslie
    1918   The Havasupai of Cataract Canyon. *American Museum Jour-
            nal* 18:636–645.
    1922a   A suggested origin for Gentile organizations. *American
            Anthropologist* 24:487–489.
    1922b   Havasupai days. In *American Indian Life,* E. C. Parsons, ed.,
            pp. 179–187. B. W. Huebsch, Inc., New York. Reprinted in
            1967 by University of Nebraska Press, Lincoln.
    1924   Havasupai texts. *International Journal of American Linguistics*
            3:109–116.
    1928   Havasupai ethnography. *American Museum of Natural His-
            tory, Anthropological Papers* 29:81–392.

1929   Problems arising from the cultural position of the Havasupai. *American Anthropologist* 31(2):213–222.
1933   *Yuman tribes of the Gila River.* University of Chicago Press,
Chicago.
1937   The association test as a method of defining religious concepts. *American Anthropologist*, 29:267–270.
1946   *Comparative vocabularies and parallel texts in two Yuman languages* [Havasupai and Maricopa] *of Arizona. University of
New Mexico Publications in Anthropology* 2.
1955   Mohave culture items. Museum of Northern Arizona,
Flagstaff, *Bulletin* 28.
Stacy, J. K.
1935   Cataract Canyon, the home of the Supai. Unpublished,
nine-page typescript, submitted to Edwin D. McKee for criticism. In files of Grand Canyon Natural History Association, Grand Canyon, Arizona.
Stephen, Alexander M.
1936   *Hopi journal.* 2 vols., Elsie Clews Parsons, ed. *Columbia University Contributions to Anthropology* 23. Columbia University Press, New York.
Steward, Julian H.
1938   *Basin-Plateau aboriginal socio-political groups.* Bureau of Ethnology, Washington, D. C., *Bulletin* 120.
Thompson, S. V., and Jack D. Smith
1968   *Evaluation Report—Havasupai Trading Company.* U.S.
Department of the Interior, Bureau of Indian Affairs, Area
Office, Phoenix.
Time Magazine
1974   Indians and the Canyon. August 12, 104(7):65.
Tucker, Sara Jones
1938   Report on the Walapai Indians. Unpublished manuscript.
prepared for the Atchison, Topeka and Santa Fe Railway
Company.
United States Department of the Interior, Bureau of Indian Affairs
1957a   *Constitution and by-laws of the Havasupai Tribe of the Hava-
supai Reservation, Arizona.* Gov. Printing Office Washington,
D. C.
1957b   *Corporate structure of the Havasupai Tribe of the Havasupai
Reservation, Arizona.* Gov. Printing Office, Washington, D. C.
United States Department of the Interior, Office of Indian Affairs
1928   *The Havasupai Indian Agency, Arizona.* Gov. Printing Office,
Washington, D.C.
United States Indian Claims Commission.
1974   Commission findings. In *Havasupai Indians*, Robert A. Manners, ed., pages 329–356. Garland Publishing, New York.

Van Tyne, Josselyn, and Andrew J. Berger.
  1959   *Fundamentals of ornithology.* John Wiley and Sons, New York.
Voegelin, C. F.
  1941   North American Indian languages still spoken and their
         genetic relationships. In *Language, culture, and personality,*
         Leslie Spier, A. Irving Hallowell, and Stanley S. Newman,
         eds., pages 15–40. American Anthropological Association,
         Menasha, Wisconsin.
Voegelin, C. F., and F. M. Voegelin
  1966   *Map of North American Indian languages.* American Eth-
         nological Society, Revised Publication 20.
  1977   *Classification and index of the world's languages.* Elsevier, New
         York.
Voegelin, C. F.; F. M. Voegelin; and Noel W. Schutz, Jr.
  1967   The language situation in Arizona as part of the Southwest
         culture area. In *Studies in southwestern ethnolinguistics,* Dell H.
         Hymes and William E. Bittle, eds., pages 403–451. Mouton
         Publishers, The Hague.
Wampler, Joseph C.
  1959a *Havasu Canyon: gem of the Grand Canyon.* Howell-North
         Press, Berkeley, California.
  1959b Whence the Havasu? *Pacific Discovery* 12(4):24–27.
Wares, Alan C.
  1968   *A comparative study of Yuman consonantism.* Mouton Pub-
         lishers, The Hague.
Whipple, A. W.
  1856   *Report of Exploration of a railway route near the thirty-fifth par-
         allel of north latitude, from the Mississippi River to the Pacific
         Ocean.* United States Pacific Railroad Explorations. House
         Ex. Doc. 91, 33rd Cong., 2nd Sess. Gov. Printing Office,
         Washington, D.C.
Whiting, Alfred F.
  1938– *Alfred F. Whiting Havasupai Archives* (P. David Seaman, c/o
  1978   Department of Anthropology, Northern Arizona Univer-
         sity, Flagstaff, Arizona; owner/collator). Approximately
         7,000 pages of Whiting's study and field notes relating to the
         Havasupai, provisionally sorted into: Bibliography, 2 bind-
         ers, 600 pages; Culture, 3 binders, 1,000 pages; Culture
         Change, 1 binder, 500 pages; Ethnobotany, 2 binders, 600
         pages; Ethnozoology, 1 binder, 350 pages; Geography, 2
         binders, 550 pages; History, 2 binders, 700 pages; Lan-
         guage, 2 binders, 900 pages; Population and People, 1
         binder, 400 pages; *Havasupai Habitat* notes and drafts, 3
         binders, 1,400 pages; Whiting recordings of interviews with
         various Havasupai individuals, approximately forty 78-rpm
         records.

1939   *Ethnobotany of the Hopi.* Museum of Northern Arizona, Flagstaff, *Bulletin* 15.

1942   Junipers of the Flagstaff region. *Plateau* 15:23–32.

1943   *Havasupai population problems.* Unpublished manuscript, based upon the annual reports of the Commissioner of Indian Affairs and other sources.

1948   John D. Lee and the Havasupai. *Plateau* 21:12–16.

1958   Havasupai characteristics in the Cohonina. *Plateau* 30(3): 55–60. [Dartmouth College Museum Scientific Contribution No. 6.]

Willey, Day Allen

1912   Dwellers of the depths. *Outdoor World and Recreation* (December 1912). Quoted in *Bulletin of the Pan American Union* 36 (April 1913):590–593.

Winter, Werner

1957   Yuman languages I. *International Journal of American Linguistics* 23:18–23.

1967   The identity of the Paipai (Akwa'ala). In *Studies in southwestern ethnolinguistics,* Dell H. Hymes and William E. Bittle, eds., pages 372–378. Mouton Publishers, The Hague.

Zaphiris, Alexander G.

1968   *The Havasupai Survey: A study of the attitudes of socio-economic conditions of an American Indian tribe.* Unpublished manuscript. University of Denver Graduate School of Social Work, Denver, Colorado.

Index

The notation HW throughout the Index designates words in the Havasupai language.

282 Index

Lagenaria vulgaris. See Gourd
Lakatova (HW). See Pear
Lampropeltis, getulus. See Snake,
   common king
Lampropeltis, pyromelana. See Snake,
   mountain king
Land use, 125–126
Language, history of, 16–20;
   morphology of, 24–25; phonetics,
   20–23
Larrea divaricata. See Creosote bush
Latrodectus mactans. See Spider, black
   widow
Leisure-time activities: dances, 90–91,
   137–139; games, 92–95; intoxicants,
   96; raiding and warfare, 97–99;
   storytelling, 92; sweatlodge, 88–90;
   tobacco, 95–96
Lemon-scented marigold (Pectis
   angustfifolia), 249. HW: 'Iwila' saha
Leo, 155
Lepidium lasiocarpum. See Peppergrass
Lepus californicus. See Rabbit, jackrabbit
Leucelene ericoides. See Aster, white
Libellula quadrimaculata. See Dragonfly.
Lice, 169. HW: He' il
Lichens, 204. HW: Hamusukwaale
Lippa, 115. See Wright lippa
Lizard, collared (Crotaphytus collaris),
   174 (HW: Tuvuna' a); desert spiny
   (Sceloporus magister), 175 (HW:
   Taathila' kuvete' e '); eastern fence (S.
   undulatus), 175 (HW: Taathila');
   short-horned (Phrynosoma douglasii),
   174 (HW: Telqwam)
Loco weed (Astragalus spp.), 226
Locusts, 169. HW: Kumpammka
Loggerhead Shrike, 185. HW: Sa' oseiya
Lonchaeidae. See Fly, biting
Lophortyx gambelii. See Gambel's Quail
Lotus mearnsii. See Deer vetch
Lycium pallidum. See Desert thorn
Lycopersicon esculentum. See Tomato
Lynx rufus. See Bobcat

Madiika (HW). See Bean, kidney;
   Rocky Mountain beeweed
Madiika' i' ma' a (HW). See Black-eyed
   pea
Maidenhair fern (Adiantum capillus-
   veneris), 204, 219. HW:
   Aha' yavinymi' i

Malus sylvestris. See Apple
Mariposa (Calochortus nuttallii), 212.
   HW: Qwakamana'
Marriage, 104–105, 106. See also
   Courtship
Marrubium vulgare. See Hoarhound
Masticophus bilineatus. See Snake,
   whipsnake
Matahaiya' imaa' a (HW). See
   Hedgehog cactus
Matahai yalo' a (HW). See Wild
   buckwheat
Mataki' i (HW). See Apache plume
Matemu' u (HW). See Arrowweed
Matko' udoo' o (HW), 251
M.B. (informant), 237, 238
Meadowrue (Thalictrum fendleri),
   204, 219
Medicago sativa. See Alfalfa
Medicine, 114–117. See also Health
   problems, treatment of
Meleagris gallopavo. See Turkey,
   Merriam's
Melilotus spp. See Clover, sweet
Melon (Cucumis melo), 33, 48, 243.
   HW: Meloona'
Meloona' (HW). See Melon;
   Muskmelon; Cantaloupe
Menstruation, customs concerning,
   105, 113
Mentzelia albicaulis. See Blazing star
Mephitis mephitis. See Skunk, striped
Mescal (Agave utahensis), 26, 48, 49, 50,
   58, 62–64. 66, 70, 72, 101, 102, 142, 160,
   172, 210, 212, 230, 233. HW: Viyale
Mesquite (Prosopis juliflora), 26, 48, 51,
   66, 77, 78, 109, 140, 228. HW: Anaala
Miinmiine' (HW). See Hummingbirds
Milky Way (HW: Yemtava), 154
Mimulus cardinalis. See Crimson
   monkey flower
Minerals, 158–164
M.M. (informant), 199, 204, 209, 214,
   215, 219–221, 226, 228, 229, 234, 235,
   240, 242–244, 246, 249, 254
Mohave Indians: and bark belts, 236;
   and dances, 91; dwellings of, 81; as
   enemies of Havasupai, 11; language
   of, 16, 17, 177; rituals of, 136; and
   rodeos, 196; songs of, 136; territory of,
   151; and trade, 37, 81, 103, 167, 211,
   227, 228
Mono Canyon, 8, 12

DATE DUE

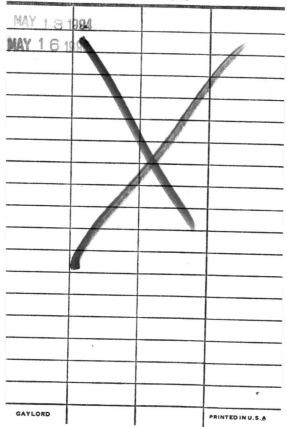

MAY 1 3 1994		
MAY 1 6 199		